Math in Focus®

Singapore Math
by Marshall Cavendish

Teacher's Guide to Transition

For New Program Implementation • Grades 2–5

Marshall Cavendish
Education

Houghton
Mifflin
Harcourt

Contents

Contents

Contents

Introduction

The *Math in Focus®: Singapore Math Teacher's Guide to Transition* provides a map for teachers and math supervisors to help students in Grades 2 to 5 transition into the *Math in Focus®* program. This guide allows teachers to easily scan the development of skills and concepts taught in prior years by including applicable Chapter Wrap Ups from across the grade levels. Instructional Pathway charts are also provided to indicate where to find additional support for transition using materials from an earlier grade, thus ensuring that students will develop the necessary background skills and concepts to help them succeed in this program.

The Guide addresses three key areas:

- **Number and Operations,** emphasizing the topics where *Math in Focus®* is accelerated relative to most math programs.

- **Model Drawing in Problem Solving,** a powerful problem-solving strategy that may be unfamiliar to teachers and students, which is used throughout *Math in Focus®*.

- **Mental Math,** a skill with much greater emphasis in *Math in Focus®* than in most programs.

These three areas were chosen because of their uniqueness to *Math in Focus®* and the Singapore approach. They are topics that are either introduced earlier than in other programs or are presented differently in this program.

The Guide offers a condensed summary of these topics by showing the appropriate Chapter Wrap Up pages from the student books. The Instructional Pathway charts are used in conjunction with Chapter Wrap Up charts (also referred to as Anchor charts) to provide transition guidance and indicate additional transition support materials.

Instructional Pathway for Transition

Grade 4: Chapters 7 and 8

Chapter 7: Decimals and Chapter 8: Adding and Subtracting Decimals

Transition Topic: Money and Decimals

Grade 4 Chapters 7–8 Pre-Test Items	Grade 4 Chapters 7–8 Pre-Test Item Objective	Additional Support for the Objective: Grade 3 Reteach	Additional Support for the Objective: Grade 3 Extra Practice	Grade 3 Teacher Edition Support	Going Back Further (Grade 2)
Chapter 7 Items 4; 5–8; 9–12	Use rounding to estimate sums and differences.	3A pp. 31–34	Lesson 2.4	3A Chapter 2 Lesson 4	2B Chapter 10 Lesson 5
Chapter 7 Items 2; 3	Identify numerator and denominator.	3B p. 84	Lesson 14.1	3B Chapter 14 Lesson 1	Grade 2 students study parts of a fraction but not their formal names in 2B Chapter 12 Lesson 1
Chapter 7 Item 1	Use models to identify equivalent fractions.	3B pp. 85–87	Lesson 14.2	3B Chapter 14 Lesson 3	
Chapter 7 Item 1	Use a number line to identify equivalent fractions.	3B p. 88	Lesson 14.2	3B Chapter 14 Lesson 2	
Chapter 7 Items 13–16	Use multiplication and division to find equivalent fractions.	3B pp. 89–96	Lesson 14.3	3B Chapter 14 Lesson 3	
Chapter 7 Items 17–18	Compare and order fractions.	3B pp. 97–106	Lesson 14.4	3B Chapter 14 Lesson 4	2B Chapter 12 Lesson 2
Chapter 8 Items 2–9	Read and write numbers to 1,000 in standard form, expanded form, and word form.	3A pp. 1–2; 5–9 See also Gr. 2B pp. 35–37; 41–44	Lessons 1.1 and 1.2 See also Gr. 2 Lessons 11.1 and 11.2.	3A Chapter 1 Lesson 1	2A Chapter 1 Lesson 2
Chapter 8 Item 1	Subtract from three-digit numbers with regrouping in hundreds, tens, and ones.	3A pp. 59–64	Lesson 4.3	3A Chapter 4 Lesson 3	2A Chapter 3 Lesson 3
Chapter 8 Items 3–4; 5–9	Add money in different ways without regrouping.	3B pp. 1–3	Lesson 10.1	3B Chapter 10 Lesson 1	2B Chapter 11 Lesson 1 (informal)
	Add money in different ways with regrouping.	3B pp. 9–11; 15–16	Lesson 10.1	3B Chapter 10 Lesson 1	2B Chapter 11 Lesson 1 (informal)
	Subtract money in different ways without regrouping.	3B pp. 17–21	Lesson 10.2	3B Chapter 10 Lesson 2	
	Subtract money in different ways with regrouping.	3B pp. 25–28; 29–30	Lesson 10.2	3B Chapter 10 Lesson 2	

For Additional Support: See the Grade 4 Chapters 7 and 8 Math in Focus Background Videos on Think Central <www.k6.thinkcentral.com>.

About this Guide

The *Teacher's Guide to Transition* provides the tools to transition with fidelity to the *Math in Focus*®: Singapore Math program by providing "Instructional Pathway" charts to pinpoint where number and operation concepts and skills are introduced in the program then follow their development throughout the grades.

For further understanding of the *Math in Focus*® program, an informative video, "Transitioning to Math in Focus" provides an overview of the pedagogy and can be found at http://www.thinkcentral.com/

Using this Guide

Follow the steps laid out here to gain maximum efficiency from this guide. Instructional Pathway charts are provided for chapters that require transitioning to the *Math in Focus*® approach.

- First: Assign the chapter pretest to identify missing prerequisite knowledge from the previous year.

- Second: Refer to the Instructional Pathway chart for that chapter. Find the objectives on which students need transition assistance, then look at the column heads to determine where to find support materials. Print out any necessary chapter Reteach and Extra Practice Support materials.

- Third: See the trajectory of lessons for the math topic by referring to the anchor charts (Chapter Wrap Ups), which trace the development of the concept. A chapter overview is provided to highlight key aspects of the instructional approach.

- Fourth: Chapter Background Videos found at http://www.thinkcentral.com/ can provide additional support.

In the course of transitioning to *Math in Focus*®, have students use concrete objects to trace the learning path from concrete, pictorial, to abstract. This process of learning is at the core of Math in Focus.

Note for Students Entering in Grade 2

Children new to the program in Grade 2 can profit by spending more time on the Recall Prior Knowledge for the chapters involving numbers and operations. Teaching these examples over one or two days, rather than having children review them on their own, should be sufficient for most children. Children who completed Books 1A and 1B the previous year should need less time on these two reviews.

Whole Numbers and Place Value

Much of the success of the Singapore approach is due to the careful way in which algorithms are developed, moving from concrete models to pictorial representations to abstract number sentences. Concepts are introduced earlier and more concretely than in many programs. For example, multiplication and division concepts are introduced in Grade 1 by having children count and form equal groups using models, without the use of formal language. Thus, by the time children are in Grade 2 they have solidified their understanding of equal groups and are ready to learn more efficient methods for counting and forming equal groups.

To ensure that all your students can experience these rich early experiences with numbers, the following pages have been compiled to help you guide students new to the program.

Whole Numbers and Place Value

Students gradually expand the set of whole numbers that they can read, write, and represent to 100,000 in Grade 4. Through the use of models such as connecting cubes, place-value blocks, and later place-value chips, they deepen their understanding of the place value system.

Tens	Ones
1	4

Grade 1

Most children come into Grade 1 knowing how to read, write, and represent the numbers 0 to 20, so the early focus with small numbers is on finding 1 more or 1 less, comparing numbers, and recognizing and making number patterns. Children also learn to recognize the numbers 11 to 20 as 1 group of ten and a particular group of ones.

	Tens	Ones
11		
13		
16		

In the second half of the year, children expand their knowledge of whole numbers to 40 and then to 120. Using place-value blocks, they learn to break these numbers into tens and ones to compare them.

Grade 2

Children learn to represent numbers to 1,000 in all three forms: word form, standard form, and expanded form, as shown below.

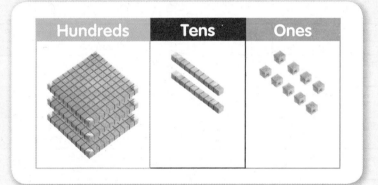

Hundreds	Tens	Ones

Word form: three hundred twenty-nine
Standard form: 329
Expanded form: 300 + 20 + 9

Children also learn to count on or count back by tens or hundreds from any given number. For example, they learn to extend and complete patterns such as the following:

362, 372, 382, ___, ___, ___
785, 685, ___, 485, ___, ___

These skills help to prepare children for mental math operations later in the year.

Grade 3   Grade 4

Students are introduced to numbers up to 10,000 in Grade 3 and up to 100,000 in Grade 4. They continue their work with comparing and ordering whole numbers and extending and completing place value patterns. In Grade 4, students learn to model these greater numbers using place-value chips instead of place-value blocks. For example, the number 47,025 is shown.

Ten Thousands	Thousands	Hundreds	Tens	Ones
●●●●	●●●●●●●●		●●	●●●●●

The place-value chips are used later in Grade 4 to develop the algorithms for multi-digit multiplication and division.

Instructional Pathway for Transition

Grade 2: Chapter 1

Chapter 1: Numbers to 1,000

Transition Topic: Whole Numbers and Place Value

Grade 2 Chapter 1 Pre-Test Items	Grade 2 Chapter 1 Pre-Test Item Objective	Additional Support for the Objective: Grade 1 Reteach	Additional Support for the Objective: Grade 1 Extra Practice	Grade 1 Teacher Edition Support	Going Back Further (Grade K)
	Compare two sets of objects by using one-to-one correspondence.	1A pp. 9–15	Lesson 1.2	1A Chapter 1 Lesson 1	KA Chapter 2 Lesson 6
Items 1–3, 11–13	Identify the number that is greater than or less than another number.	1A pp. 9–16	Lesson 1.2	1B Chapter 16 Lesson 3	KA Chapter 6 Lesson 5
Items 1–3, 11–13	Compare numbers to 120.	1B pp. 133–137	Lesson 16.3	1B Chapter 16 Lesson 3	KB Chapter 18 Lesson 2 (numbers to 10 only)
Items 4–5	Read and write 41 to 120 in numbers and words.	1B pp. 126–127	Lesson 16.1	1B Chapter 16 Lesson 2	KB Chapter 8 Lesson 7 (numerals only)
Item 6	Find different number bonds for numbers to 10.	1A pp. 21–28	Lesson 2.1	1A Chapter 2	KB Chapter 12 Lesson 1 (informal)
Item 7	Show objects up to 40 as tens and ones.	1B pp. 37–40	Lesson 12.2	1B Chapter 12 Lesson 2	KB Chapter 8 Lesson 3 (informal)
Item 7	Show objects up to 120 as tens and ones.	1B pp. 121–125	Lesson 16.2	1B Chapter 16 Lesson 2	
Items 8, 10	Subtract a one-digit from a two-digit number with and without regrouping.	1A pp. 145–148	Lesson 8.2	1B Chapter 17 Lessons 3–4	KB Chapter 18 Lesson 2 (numbers to 10 only)
Item 9	Use different strategies to add one- and two-digit numbers.	1A pp. 127–136	Lesson 8.1	1B Chapter 17 Lessons 1–2	KB Chapter 17 Lesson 1 (one-digit only)
Items 14–16	Find the missing numbers in a number pattern.	1B pp. 140–141	Lesson 16.3	1B Chapter 16 Lessons 1–3	KB Chapter 8 Lesson 7
	Use ordinal numbers.	1A pp 97–100	Lesson 6.1	1A Chapter 6 Lesson 1	KB Chapter 10 Lesson 3
	Use as place-value chart to show numbers up to 100.	1B pp 129–132	Lesson 16.2	1B Chapter 16 Lesson 2	

For Additional Support: See the Grade 2 Chapter 1 Math in Focus Background Videos on Think Central <www-k6.thinkcentral.com>.

Whole Numbers and Place Value

Students have learned...

BIG IDEA

Count, compare, and order numbers to 20.

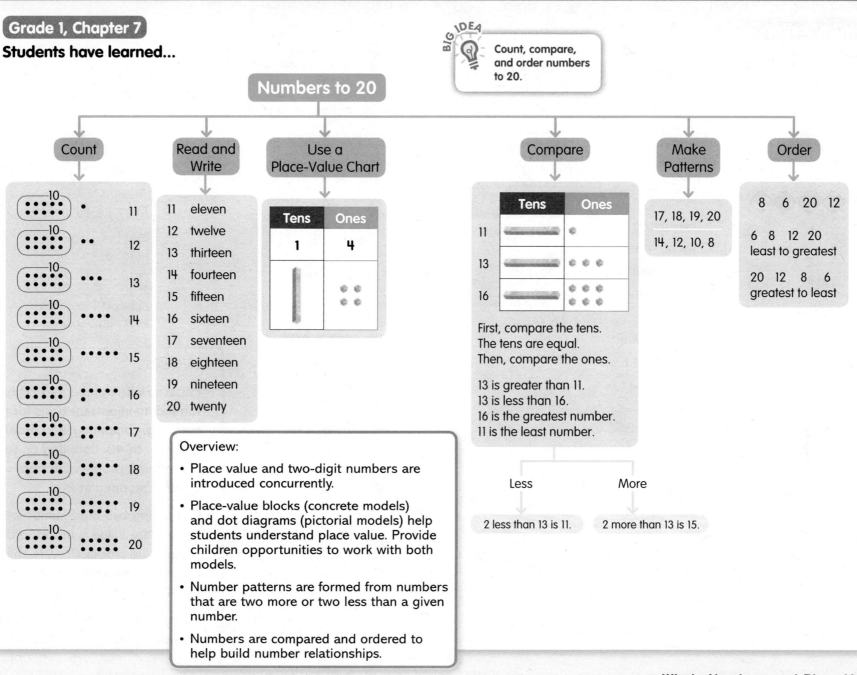

Numbers to 20

Count

10 ⚫⚫⚫⚫⚫	⚫	11
10 ⚫⚫⚫⚫⚫	⚫⚫	12
10 ⚫⚫⚫⚫⚫	⚫⚫⚫	13
10 ⚫⚫⚫⚫⚫	⚫⚫⚫⚫	14
10 ⚫⚫⚫⚫⚫	⚫⚫⚫⚫⚫	15
10 ⚫⚫⚫⚫⚫	⚫⚫⚫⚫⚫ ⚫	16
10 ⚫⚫⚫⚫⚫	⚫⚫⚫⚫⚫ ⚫⚫	17
10 ⚫⚫⚫⚫⚫	⚫⚫⚫⚫⚫ ⚫⚫⚫	18
10 ⚫⚫⚫⚫⚫	⚫⚫⚫⚫⚫ ⚫⚫⚫⚫	19
10 ⚫⚫⚫⚫⚫	⚫⚫⚫⚫⚫ ⚫⚫⚫⚫⚫	20

Read and Write

11	eleven
12	twelve
13	thirteen
14	fourteen
15	fifteen
16	sixteen
17	seventeen
18	eighteen
19	nineteen
20	twenty

Use a Place-Value Chart

Tens	Ones
1	**4**
▮	⚫⚫ ⚫⚫

Compare

	Tens	Ones
11	▬	⚫
13	▬	⚫⚫⚫
16	▬	⚫⚫⚫ ⚫⚫⚫

First, compare the tens.
The tens are equal.
Then, compare the ones.

13 is greater than 11.
13 is less than 16.
16 is the greatest number.
11 is the least number.

Less

2 less than 13 is 11.

More

2 more than 13 is 15.

Make Patterns

17, 18, 19, 20

14, 12, 10, 8

Order

8 6 20 12

6 8 12 20
least to greatest

20 12 8 6
greatest to least

Overview:

- Place value and two-digit numbers are introduced concurrently.
- Place-value blocks (concrete models) and dot diagrams (pictorial models) help students understand place value. Provide children opportunities to work with both models.
- Number patterns are formed from numbers that are two more or two less than a given number.
- Numbers are compared and ordered to help build number relationships.

Whole Numbers and Place Value

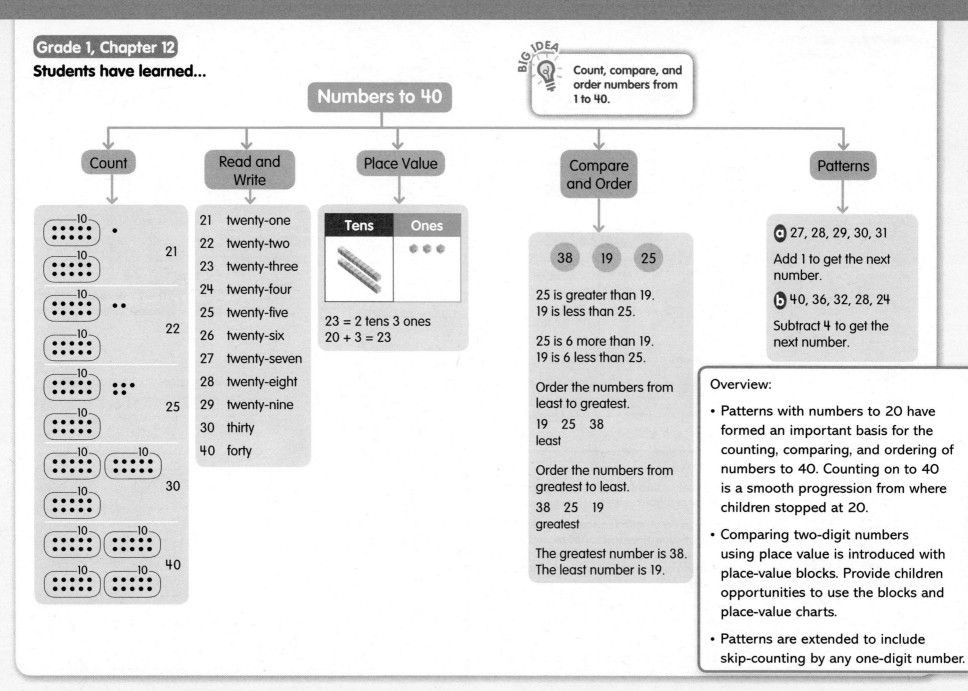

Grade 1, Chapter 12

Students have learned...

BIG IDEA

Count, compare, and order numbers from 1 to 40.

Numbers to 40

Count

21

22

25

30

40

Read and Write

21	twenty-one
22	twenty-two
23	twenty-three
24	twenty-four
25	twenty-five
26	twenty-six
27	twenty-seven
28	twenty-eight
29	twenty-nine
30	thirty
40	forty

Place Value

Tens	Ones

23 = 2 tens 3 ones
20 + 3 = 23

Compare and Order

38   19   25

25 is greater than 19.
19 is less than 25.

25 is 6 more than 19.
19 is 6 less than 25.

Order the numbers from least to greatest.
19   25   38
least

Order the numbers from greatest to least.
38   25   19
greatest

The greatest number is 38.
The least number is 19.

Patterns

ⓐ 27, 28, 29, 30, 31
Add 1 to get the next number.

ⓑ 40, 36, 32, 28, 24
Subtract 4 to get the next number.

Overview:

• Patterns with numbers to 20 have formed an important basis for the counting, comparing, and ordering of numbers to 40. Counting on to 40 is a smooth progression from where children stopped at 20.

• Comparing two-digit numbers using place value is introduced with place-value blocks. Provide children opportunities to use the blocks and place-value charts.

• Patterns are extended to include skip-counting by any one-digit number.

Whole Numbers and Place Value

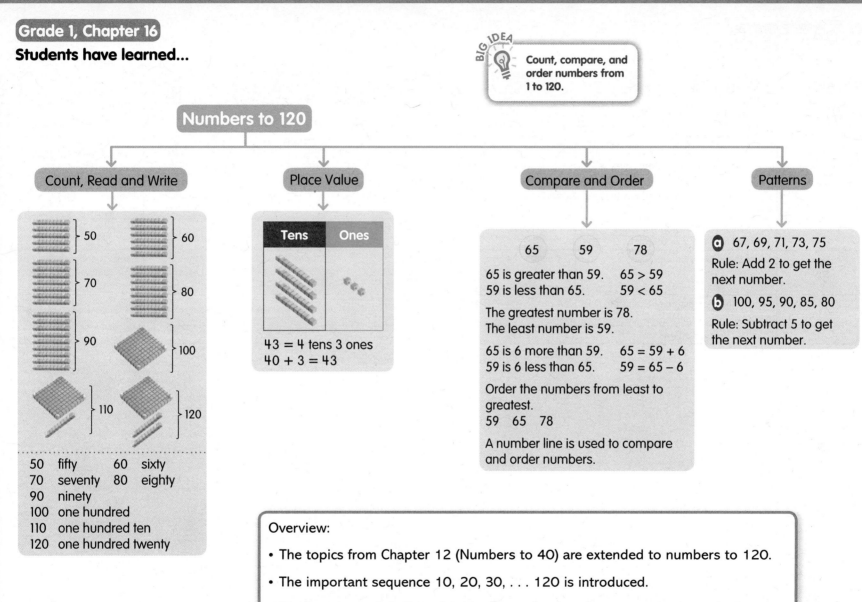

Grade 1, Chapter 16
Students have learned...

BIG IDEA Count, compare, and order numbers from 1 to 120.

Numbers to 120

Count, Read and Write

- 50
- 60
- 70
- 80
- 90
- 100
- 110
- 120

50	fifty	60	sixty
70	seventy	80	eighty
90	ninety
100	one hundred
110	one hundred ten
120	one hundred twenty

Place Value

Tens	Ones

43 = 4 tens 3 ones
40 + 3 = 43

Compare and Order

65   59   78

65 is greater than 59.   65 > 59
59 is less than 65.   59 < 65

The greatest number is 78.
The least number is 59.

65 is 6 more than 59.   65 = 59 + 6
59 is 6 less than 65.   59 = 65 − 6

Order the numbers from least to greatest.
59   65   78

A number line is used to compare and order numbers.

Patterns

a 67, 69, 71, 73, 75
Rule: Add 2 to get the next number.

b 100, 95, 90, 85, 80
Rule: Subtract 5 to get the next number.

Overview:

- The topics from Chapter 12 (Numbers to 40) are extended to numbers to 120.

- The important sequence 10, 20, 30, . . . 120 is introduced.

- Students extend their work with place value, number comparisons, and patterns.

Grade 3: Chapter 1

Chapter 1: Numbers to 10,000

Transition Topic: Whole Numbers and Place Value

Grade 3 Chapter 1 Pre-Test Items	Grade 3 Chapter 1 Pre-Test Item Objective	Additional Support for the Objective: Grade 2 Reteach	Additional Support for the Objective: Grade 2 Extra Practice	Grade 2 Teacher Edition Support	Going Back Further (Grade 1)
Items 3–5; 8–9	Read and write numbers to 1,000 in standard form, expanded form, and word form.	2A pp. 13–14	Lesson 1.2	2A Chapter 1 Lesson 1	Grade 1 students study numbers to 120 in Chapter 16 Lesson 1
Items 1–2, 14-15	Compare numbers using the terms **greater than** and **less than**.	2A pp. 15; 20	Lesson 1.3	2A Chapter 1 Lesson 3	1B Chapter 16 Lesson 3
Items 14–15; 17	Order three-digit numbers.	2A pp. 21–24	Lesson 1.4	2A Chapter 1 Lesson 4	Grade 1 students order two-digit numbers in Chapter 16 Lesson 3
Item 16	Identify the greatest number and the least number.	2A pp. 21–22	Lesson 1.4	2A Chapter 1 Lesson 4	1B Chapter 16 Lesson 3
Items 10–13	Identify number patterns.	2A pp. 8; 24	Lesson 1.4	2A Chapter 1 Lesson 4	1B Chapter 16 Lesson 3

For Additional Support: See the Grade 3 Chapter 1 Math in Focus Background Videos on Think Central <www-k6.thinkcentral.com>.

Whole Numbers and Place Value

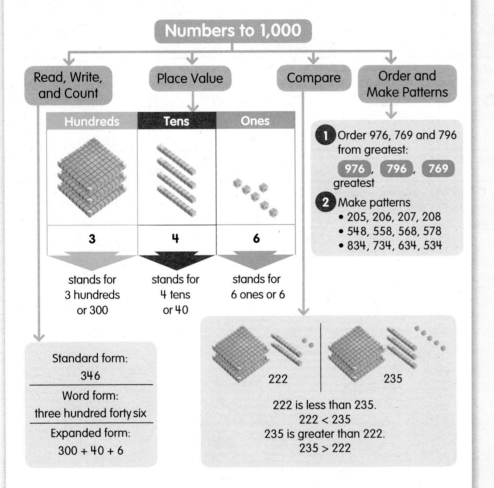

Grade 2, Chapter 1
Students have learned...

Numbers to 1,000

- Read, Write, and Count
- Place Value
- Compare
- Order and Make Patterns

Hundreds	Tens	Ones
3	4	6
stands for 3 hundreds or 300	stands for 4 tens or 40	stands for 6 ones or 6

Standard form:
346

Word form:
three hundred forty six

Expanded form:
300 + 40 + 6

1 Order 976, 769 and 796 from greatest:

976 , 796 , 769
greatest

2 Make patterns
- 205, 206, 207, 208
- 548, 558, 568, 578
- 834, 734, 634, 534

222   235

222 is less than 235.
222 < 235
235 is greater than 222.
235 > 222

Overview:

- Base-ten blocks, place-value charts, and number lines are used to develop the association between the physical representation of the number, the number symbol, and the number word. At this stage, children are still shown the concrete representation to help them better understand the concepts of numbers.

- Numbers to 1,000 are modeled with place-value blocks. Provide children opportunities to work with place-value blocks to firmly establish the concrete phase of learning about numbers to 1,000.

- The number represented by a model is expressed in three ways: standard form, word form, and expanded form.

- Number comparisons are extended to these greater numbers and to using multiple comparisons to order a set of numbers.

- The rule for a pattern can increase or decrease by 10 or 100, starting from any number.

Grade 4: Chapter 1

Chapter 1: Place Value of Whole Numbers

Transition Topic: Whole Numbers and Place Value

Grade 4 Chapter 1 Pre-Test Items	Grade 4 Chapter 1 Pre-Test Item Objective	Additional Support for the Objective: Grade 3 Reteach	Additional Support for the Objective: Grade 3 Extra Practice	Grade 3 Teacher Edition Support	Going Back Further (Grade 2)
Items 1–7; 9–11	Read and write numbers to 10,000 in standard form, expanded form, and word form.	3A pp. 1–10	Lessons 1.1 and 1.2	3A Chapter 1 Lesson 2	Grade 2 students read and write numbers to 1,000 in 2A Chapter 1 Lesson 2
Items 12–14; 17	Compare and order numbers	3A pp. 11–16; See also 2A pp. 16–20	Lesson 1.3	3A Chapter 1 Lesson 3	2A Chapter 1 Lesson 3

For Additional Support: See the Grade 4 Chapter 1 Math in Focus Background Videos on Think Central <www-k6.thinkcentral.com>.

Grade 3, Chapter 1

Students have learned...

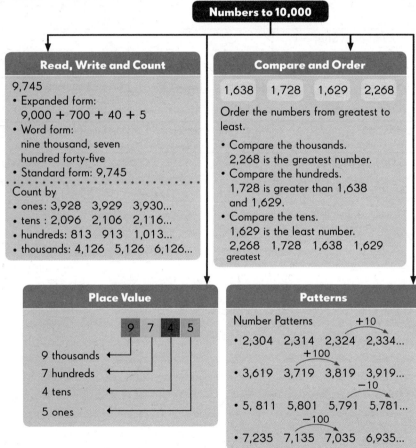

Numbers to 10,000

Read, Write and Count

9,745
- Expanded form:
  9,000 + 700 + 40 + 5
- Word form:
  nine thousand, seven
  hundred forty-five
- Standard form: 9,745

Count by
- ones: 3,928   3,929   3,930...
- tens : 2,096   2,106   2,116...
- hundreds: 813   913   1,013...
- thousands: 4,126   5,126   6,126...

Compare and Order

1,638   1,728   1,629   2,268

Order the numbers from greatest to least.

- Compare the thousands.
  2,268 is the greatest number.
- Compare the hundreds.
  1,728 is greater than 1,638
  and 1,629.
- Compare the tens.
  1,629 is the least number.

2,268   1,728   1,638   1,629
greatest

Place Value

9 7 4 5

9 thousands ←
7 hundreds ←
4 tens ←
5 ones ←

Patterns

Number Patterns   +10
- 2,304   2,314   2,324   2,334...
            +100
- 3,619   3,719   3,819   3,919...
                    −10
- 5, 811   5,801   5,791   5,781...
       −100
- 7,235   7,135   7,035   6,935...

Overview:

- In Grade 2, children learned to count, read, and write numbers up to 1,000. In Grade 3, numbers to 10,000 are modeled and represented in three forms.

- Base-ten blocks are used to develop the association between the physical representation of the number, the numeral, and the number word.

- Sets of four numbers, ranging up to 10,000, are ordered.

- Number patterns are extended to these greater numbers.

Grade 5: Chapter 1

Chapter 1: Whole Numbers

Transition Topic: Whole Numbers and Place Value

Grade 5 Chapter 1 Pre-Test Items	Grade 5 Chapter 1 Pre-Test Item Objective	Additional Support for the Objective: Grade 4 Reteach	Additional Support for the Objective: Grade 4 Extra Practice	Grade 4 Teacher Edition Support	Going Back Further (Grade 3)
Items 1; 5–8	Write numbers to 100,000 in standard form, word form, and expanded form.	4A pp. 1–7	Lesson 1.1	4A Chapter 1 Lesson 1	Grade 3 students write numbers to 10,000 in 3A Chapter 1 Lesson 2
Items 2, 9–10, 18	Compare and order numbers to 100,000.	4A pp. 15–18	Lesson 1.2	4A Chapter 1 Lesson 2	3A Chapter 1 Lesson 3 (to 10,000)

For Additional Support: See the Grade 5 Chapter 1 Math in Focus Background Videos on Think Central <www-k6.thinkcentral.com>.

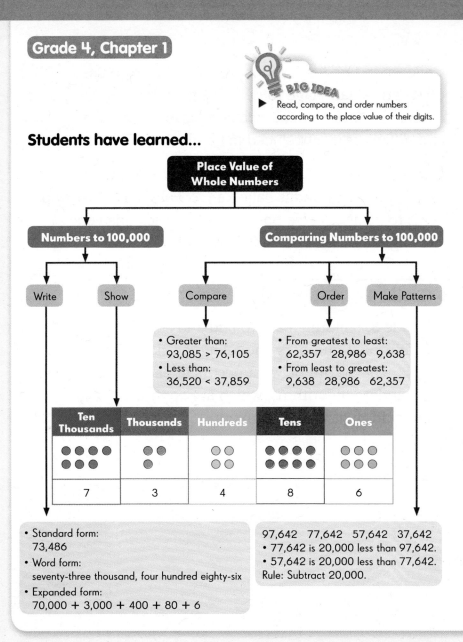

Grade 4, Chapter 1

BIG IDEA

▶ Read, compare, and order numbers according to the place value of their digits.

Students have learned...

Place Value of Whole Numbers

Numbers to 100,000

Write

Show

Comparing Numbers to 100,000

Compare

Order

Make Patterns

- Greater than:
  93,085 > 76,105
- Less than:
  36,520 < 37,859

- From greatest to least:
  62,357   28,986   9,638
- From least to greatest:
  9,638   28,986   62,357

Ten Thousands	Thousands	Hundreds	Tens	Ones
●●●●● ●●●	●● ●	○○ ○○	●●●● ●●●●	○○○ ○○○
7	3	4	8	6

- Standard form:
  73,486
- Word form:
  seventy-three thousand, four hundred eighty-six
- Expanded form:
  70,000 + 3,000 + 400 + 80 + 6

97,642   77,642   57,642   37,642
- 77,642 is 20,000 less than 97,642.
- 57,642 is 20,000 less than 77,642.
Rule: Subtract 20,000.

Overview:

- In Grade 3, children learned to represent numbers to 10,000 in different equivalent forms.

- Now numbers to 100,000 are modeled with place-value chips, a more advanced model for whole numbers, since a single chip can represent any power of 10, such as 1, 10, 100, and so on.

- This model is used later in the year to develop the algorithms for multi-digit multiplication and multi-digit division.

- The rules for number patterns can be any multiple of 10, 100, or 1,000.

Addition and Subtraction of Whole Numbers

Addition and Subtraction of Whole Numbers

Addition and subtraction skills are introduced earlier in *Math in Focus®*: Singapore Math than in many elementary programs. Children should know their basic addition and subtraction facts by the end of Grade 1 and should be competent with multi-digit addition and subtraction by the end of Grade 2. These skills are extended in Grades 3 and 4, using greater numbers.

Grade 1 | Grade 2

Children learn addition and subtraction strategies to help them make connections among small numbers and to aid recall of addition and subtraction facts. Some of the strategies they use are counting on, counting back, and composing and decomposing numbers using number bonds. A *number bond* is a way of showing a part-part-whole model, as shown on the facing page.

Once children are familiar with numbers to 20, they use number bonds to help them develop number facts to 18. In the first half of the year, they learn that adding is related to joining sets and subtraction is related to taking away from a set. In the latter half of the year, subtraction as a comparison ("how many more") is introduced, as well as addition and subtraction of two-digit numbers.

Children in Grades 1 and 2 are encouraged to use their own natural language to describe these operations and operands. The mathematically precise vocabulary of *sum* and *difference* is introduced in Grade 3.

Children learn that all the number sentences they can write from a number bond is called a *fact family*. This concept leads to using inverse operations to check answers to two-digit addition and subtraction problems.

Grade 3 | Grade 4

In grade 3, children learn to add and subtract three-digit and four-digit numbers, modeling the skill with place-value blocks. The record of what occurs at each step becomes the standard algorithms, which are confirmed in grade 4 with multi-digit whole numbers.

BIG IDEA
Number bonds can be used to show parts and whole.

Number Bonds

Students have learned...

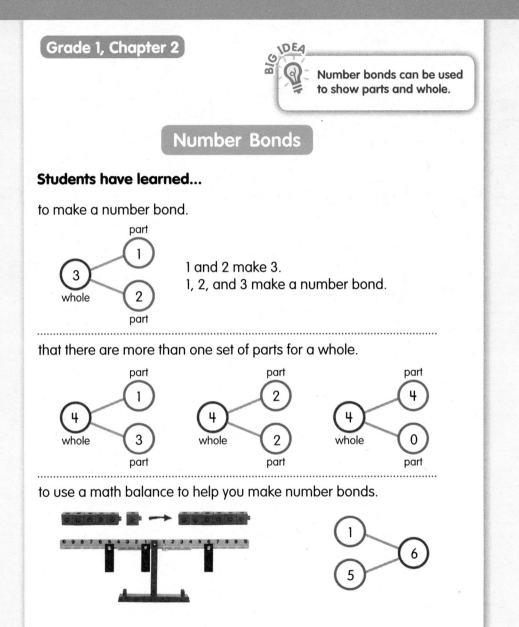

to make a number bond.

1 and 2 make 3.
1, 2, and 3 make a number bond.

that there are more than one set of parts for a whole.

to use a math balance to help you make number bonds.

Overview:

- Number bonds are a part-part-whole model and a way of thinking about a fact family, furthering understanding of number relationships.

- Number bonds are used throughout the program to develop addition and subtraction concepts, from basic facts to algorithms and mental math strategies.

- Number bonds are also used to illustrate the properties of addition and subtraction.

- Understanding number bonds will improve children's ability to do mental math and make it easier to do regrouping at a later stage.

Instructional Pathway for Transition

Grade 2: Chapters 2, 3, and 4

Chapter 2: Addition up to 1,000; Chapter 3: Subtraction up to 1,000; and Chapter 4: Using Bar Models: Addition and Subtraction

Transition Topic: Addition and Subtraction of Whole Numbers

Grade 2 Chapters 2, 3, and 4 Pre-Test Items	Grade 2 Chapters 2, 3, and 4 Pre-Test Item Objective	Additional Support for the Objective: Grade 1 Reteach	Additional Support for the Objective: Grade 1 Extra Practice	Grade 1 Teacher Edition Support	Going Back Further (Grade K)
Chapter 2 Items 1–2	Write and solve addition sentences.	1A, pp. 37–42	Lessons 3.2 and 3.3	1A Chapter 3 Lesson 1	KB Chapter 17 Lesson 2
Chapter 2 Item 4	Write fact families.	1A, pp. 63–64	Lesson 4.4	1A Chapter 4 Lesson 4	KB Chapter 14 Lesson 1
Chapter 2 Items 5–6	Add two numbers without regrouping.	1B, pp. 143–150	Lesson 17.1	1B Chapter 13 Lesson 1	KB Chapter 20 Lesson 2
Chapter 2 Item 7	Add two numbers with regrouping.	1B, pp. 61–68	Lesson 13.2	1B Chapter 17 Lesson 2	
Chapter 2 Item 8	Add three one-digit numbers.	1B, pp. 85–86	Lesson 13.5	1B Chapter 13 Lesson 5	
Chapter 2 Item 9	Solve real-world (addition) problems.	1B, pp. 87–90	Lesson 13.6	1A Chapter 8 Lesson 3	KB Chapter 17 Lesson 1
Chapter 3 Items 1, 6–7	Subtract without regrouping.	1B, pp. 159–166	Lesson 17.3	1B Chapter 14 Lesson 2	KB Chapter 18 Lesson 3
Chapter 3 Items 2, 8	Subtract with regrouping.	1B, pp. 167–172	Lesson 17.4	1B Chapter 17 Lesson 4	
Chapter 3 Item 4	Write fact families.	1A, pp. 63–64	Lesson 4.4	1A Chapter 4 Lesson 4	KB Chapter 14 Lesson 1
Chapter 3 Item 5	Write and solve addition sentences.	1A, pp. 37–42	Lessons 3.2 and 3.3	1A Chapter 3 Lesson 1	KB Chapter 17 Lesson 2
Chapter 4 Items 1–3	Identify the number that is greater than or less than another number.	1A, pp. 9–16	Lesson 1.2	1B Chapter 12 Lesson 3	KB Chapter 9 Lesson 2
Chapter 4 Items 4–5, 8–9	Add two numbers with regrouping.	1B, pp. 151–158	Lesson 17.2	1B Chapter 17 Lesson 2	
Chapter 4 Item 6	Add two numbers without regrouping.	1B, pp. 143–150	Lesson 17.1	1B Chapter 13 Lesson 1	KB Chapter 20 Lesson 2
Chapter 4 Item 7	Subtract without regrouping.	1B, pp. 159–166	Lesson 17.3	1B Chapter 14 Lesson 2	KB Chapter 18 Lesson 3
Chapter 4 Items 10–11	Subtract with regrouping.	1B, pp. 167–172	Lesson 17.4	1B Chapter 17 Lesson 4	
Chapter 4 Item 12	Solve real-world (addition) problems.	1B, pp. 87–90	Lesson 13.6	1A Chapter 8 Lesson 3	KB Chapter 17 Lesson 1
Chapter 4 Item 13	Solve real-world (subtraction) problems.	1A, pp. 143–146	Lesson 8.3	1A Chapter 8 Lesson 3	KB Chapter 18 Lesson 1

For Additional Support: See the Grade 2 Chapters 2, 3, and 4 Math in Focus Background Videos on Think Central <www-k6.thinkcentral.com>.

Grade 1, Chapter 3

Students have learned...

BIG IDEA
Addition can be used to find how many in all.

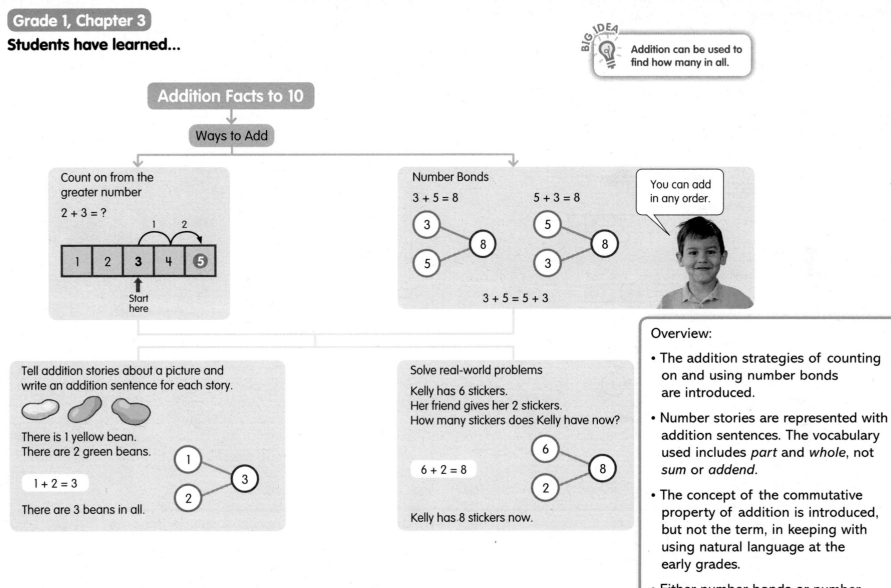

Addition Facts to 10

Ways to Add

Count on from the greater number

2 + 3 = ?

Start here

Number Bonds

3 + 5 = 8   5 + 3 = 8

3 + 5 = 5 + 3

You can add in any order.

Tell addition stories about a picture and write an addition sentence for each story.

There is 1 yellow bean.
There are 2 green beans.

1 + 2 = 3

There are 3 beans in all.

Solve real-world problems

Kelly has 6 stickers.
Her friend gives her 2 stickers.
How many stickers does Kelly have now?

6 + 2 = 8

Kelly has 8 stickers now.

Overview:

• The addition strategies of counting on and using number bonds are introduced.

• Number stories are represented with addition sentences. The vocabulary used includes *part* and *whole*, not *sum* or *addend*.

• The concept of the commutative property of addition is introduced, but not the term, in keeping with using natural language at the early grades.

• Either number bonds or number sentences can be used to solve real-world problems.

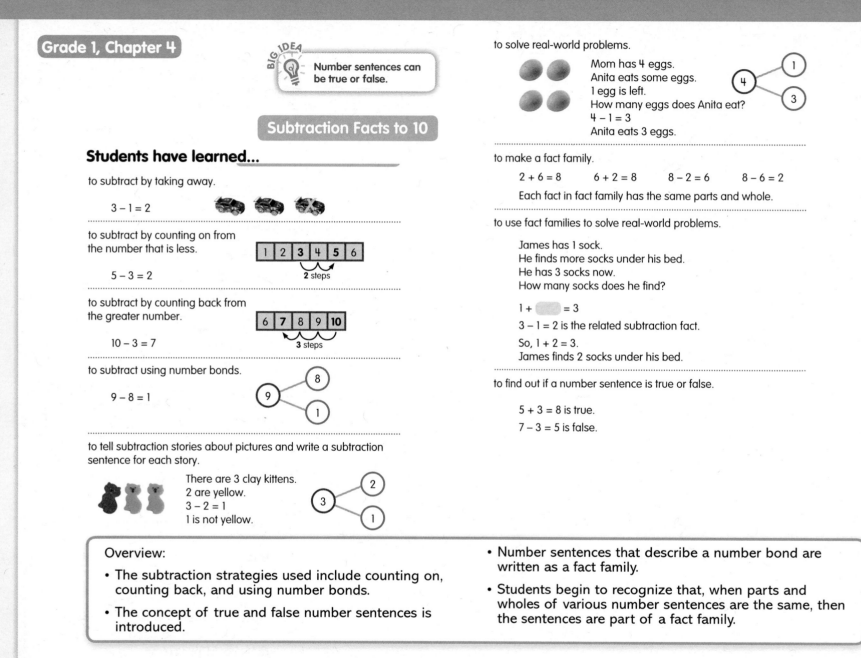

BIG IDEA Number sentences can be true or false.

Subtraction Facts to 10

Students have learned...

to subtract by taking away.

3 – 1 = 2

to subtract by counting on from the number that is less.

| 1 | 2 | **3** | 4 | **5** | 6 |

5 – 3 = 2

2 steps

to subtract by counting back from the greater number.

| 6 | **7** | 8 | 9 | **10** |

10 – 3 = 7

3 steps

to subtract using number bonds.

9 – 8 = 1

to tell subtraction stories about pictures and write a subtraction sentence for each story.

There are 3 clay kittens.
2 are yellow.
3 – 2 = 1
1 is not yellow.

to solve real-world problems.

Mom has 4 eggs.
Anita eats some eggs.
1 egg is left.
How many eggs does Anita eat?
4 – 1 = 3
Anita eats 3 eggs.

to make a fact family.

2 + 6 = 8   6 + 2 = 8   8 – 2 = 6   8 – 6 = 2

Each fact in fact family has the same parts and whole.

to use fact families to solve real-world problems.

James has 1 sock.
He finds more socks under his bed.
He has 3 socks now.
How many socks does he find?

1 + ⬤ = 3
3 – 1 = 2 is the related subtraction fact.
So, 1 + 2 = 3.
James finds 2 socks under his bed.

to find out if a number sentence is true or false.

5 + 3 = 8 is true.
7 – 3 = 5 is false.

Overview:

- The subtraction strategies used include counting on, counting back, and using number bonds.
- The concept of true and false number sentences is introduced.

- Number sentences that describe a number bond are written as a fact family.
- Students begin to recognize that, when parts and wholes of various number sentences are the same, then the sentences are part of a fact family.

Addition and Subtraction of Whole Numbers

Addition and Subtraction Facts to 20

BIG IDEA
Different strategies can be used to add and subtract.

Students have learned...

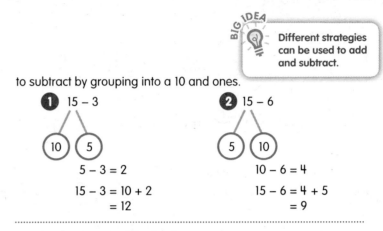

8 + 5 = 10 + 3
      = 13

8 + 5

2   3

8 + 2 = 10
↓
8 + 5 = 10 + 3
      = 13

to add by grouping into a 10 and ones.

11 + 5   5 + 1 = 6

10   1   11 + 5 = 10 + 6
                       = 16

to add using doubles facts.

3 + 3 = 6 is a doubles fact.
The numbers that are added are the same.

to add using doubles plus one.

3 + 4 is 3 + 3 plus 1
3 + 4 = 3 + 3 + 1
      = 7

Overview:
- The addition strategies of making a ten, using doubles facts, and using doubles-plus-one facts are introduced.
- The subtraction strategies of decomposing a "teen number" (using a number bond) into a ten and ones and using doubles facts are introduced.
- The addition and subtraction facts are applied to solving real-world problems.

to subtract by grouping into a 10 and ones.

1 15 − 3

10   5

5 − 3 = 2
15 − 3 = 10 + 2
       = 12

2 15 − 6

5   10

10 − 6 = 4
15 − 6 = 4 + 5
       = 9

to subtract using doubles facts.

7 + 7 = 14
So, 14 − 7 = 7.

to add or subtract to solve real-world problems.

1 Joy has 8 tadpoles.
Ben gives her 5 more tadpoles.
How many tadpoles does she have now?

8 + 5 = 13

Joy has 13 tadpoles now.

2 Con has 18 marbles.
He gives Pete 9 marbles.
How many marbles does Con have left?

18 − 9 = 9

Con has 9 marbles left.

Grade 1, Chapter 13
Students have learned...

BIG IDEA
Whole numbers can be added and subtracted with and without regrouping.

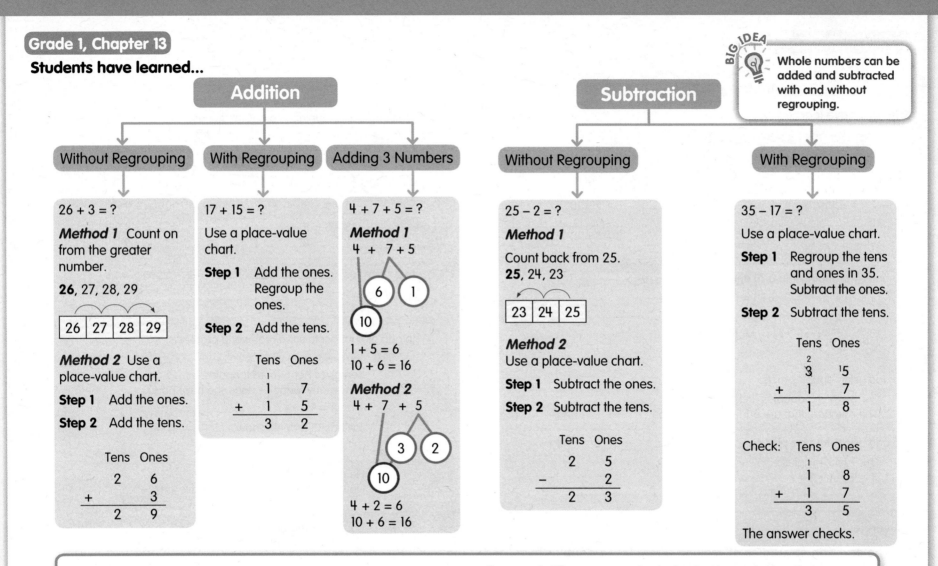

Addition

Without Regrouping

26 + 3 = ?

Method 1 Count on from the greater number.

26, 27, 28, 29

26	27	28	29

Method 2 Use a place-value chart.

Step 1 Add the ones.
Step 2 Add the tens.

Tens	Ones
2	6
+	3
2	9

With Regrouping

17 + 15 = ?

Use a place-value chart.

Step 1 Add the ones. Regroup the ones.
Step 2 Add the tens.

Tens	Ones
1	
1	7
+ 1	5
3	2

Adding 3 Numbers

4 + 7 + 5 = ?

Method 1
4 + 7 + 5
6 1
10

1 + 5 = 6
10 + 6 = 16

Method 2
4 + 7 + 5
3 2
10

4 + 2 = 6
10 + 6 = 16

Subtraction

Without Regrouping

25 – 2 = ?

Method 1

Count back from 25.
25, 24, 23

23	24	25

Method 2
Use a place-value chart.

Step 1 Subtract the ones.
Step 2 Subtract the tens.

Tens	Ones
2	5
–	2
2	3

With Regrouping

35 – 17 = ?

Use a place-value chart.

Step 1 Regroup the tens and ones in 35. Subtract the ones.
Step 2 Subtract the tens.

Tens	Ones
2	
3	15
+ 1	7
1	8

Check:

Tens	Ones
1	
1	8
+ 1	7
3	5

The answer checks.

Overview:

- The comparison meaning of subtraction is introduced. (Children learned to compare two-digit numbers in Chapter 12.)
- Addition and subtraction of two-digit numbers is introduced with place-value blocks.

- Sums and differences are checked using inverse operations.
- The process of adding three numbers is simplified by showing children how to make ten first, using number bonds.
- Once the process of regrouping ones and tens is well established, addition and subtraction are done on a place-value chart.

Addition and Subtraction of Whole Numbers

Students have learned...

BIG IDEA
Numbers to 100 can be added and subtracted with and without regrouping.

Addition

Without Regrouping

$64 + 3 = ?$

Method 1
Count on from the greater number.
64, 65, 66, 67

Method 2
Use a place-value chart.

Step 1 Add the ones.

Step 2 Add the tens.

Tens	Ones
6	4
+	3
6	7

With Regrouping

$54 + 16 = ?$

Use a place-value chart.

Step 1 Add the ones.
Regroup the ones.

Step 2 Add the tens.

Tens	Ones
¹5	4
+ 1	6
7	0

Subtraction

Without Regrouping

$75 - 2 = ?$

Method 1
Count back from 75.
75, 74, 73

Method 2
Use a place-value chart.

Step 1 Subtract the ones.

Step 2 Subtract the tens.

Tens	Ones
7	5
−	2
7	3

With Regrouping

$65 - 18 = ?$

Use a place-value chart.

Step 1 Regroup the tens and ones in 65. Subtract the ones.

Step 2 Subtract the tens.

Tens	Ones
⁵6̶	¹5
− 1	8
4	7

Overview:

• The methods of adding and subtracting numbers to 40 (from Chapter 13) are revisited, using numbers up to 100.

• Because greater numbers are more difficult to model, the addition and subtraction processes become more abstract.

• Children are encouraged to check each answer.

• Children solve problems using both meanings for subtraction: take away and comparison.

Instructional Pathway for Transition

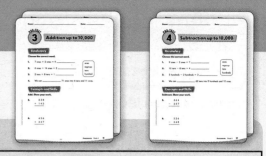

Grade 3: Chapters 3 and 4

Chapter 3: Addition to 10,000 and Chapter 4: Subtraction to 10,000

Transition Topic: Addition and Subtraction of Whole Numbers					
Grade 3 Chapters 3-4 Pre-Test Items	Grade 3 Chapters 3-4 Pre-Test Item Objective	Additional Support for the Objective: Grade 2 Reteach	Additional Support for the Objective: Grade 2 Extra Practice	Grade 2 Teacher Edition Support	Going Back Further (Grade 1)
Chapter 3 Item 1	Add up to three-digit numbers without regrouping.	2A pp. 27–38	Lesson 2.2	2A Chapter 2 Lesson 2	Grade 1 students study addition facts to 10 in 1A Chapter 3 Lesson 1
Chapter 3 Items 2; 5	Add up to three-digit numbers with regrouping in ones.	2A pp. 39–44	Lesson 2.3	2A Chapter 2 Lesson 3	Grade 1 students study 2-digit + 1-digit with regrouping in 1B Chapter 13 Lesson 2
Chapter 3 Item 3	Add up to three-digit numbers with regrouping in tens.	2A pp. 45–48	Lesson 2.4	2A Chapter 2 Lesson 4	Grade 1 students study 2-digit + 1-digit with regrouping in 1B Chapter 13 Lesson 2
Chapter 3 Items 4; 6; 7–8	Add up to three-digit numbers with regrouping in ones and tens.	2A pp. 49–52	Lesson 2.5	2A Chapter 2 Lesson 5	Grade 1 students study 2-digit + 1-digit with regrouping in 1B Chapter 13 Lesson 2
Chapter 3 Items 7–8	Solve real-world addition problems.	2A pp. 38; 43–44; 48; 52	Lesson 2.2 p. 22; Lesson 2.3 p. 24; Lesson 2.4 p. 26; Lesson 2.5 p. 28	2A Chapter 2 Lesson 4	1B Chapter 13 Lesson 6
Chapter 4 Items 1–3	Subtract from three-digit numbers without regrouping.	2A pp. 53–64	Lesson 3.1	2A Chapter 3 Lesson 1	Grade 1 students study subtraction facts to 10 in 1A Chapter 4
Chapter 4 Item 5	Subtract from three-digit numbers with regrouping in tens and ones.	2A pp. 65–70	Lesson 3.2	2A Chapter 3 Lesson 2	1B Chapter 13 Lesson 4 covers 2-digit – 1-digit with regrouping
Chapter 4 Item 4	Subtract from three-digit numbers with regrouping in hundreds and tens.	2A pp. 71–74	Lesson 3.3	2A Chapter 3 Lesson 3	
Chapter 4 Items 6; 8	Subtract from three-digit numbers with regrouping in hundreds, tens, and ones.	2A pp. 75–78	Lesson 3.4	2A Chapter 3 Lesson 4	
Chapter 4 Item 7	Subtract from three-digit numbers with zeros.	2A pp. 79–82	Lesson 3.5	2A Chapter 3 Lesson 5	
Chapter 4 Items 7–8	Solve real-world subtraction problems.	2A pp. 64; 69–70; 74; 78; 82	Lesson 3.1–3.5 pp. 32; 34; 36; 38; 40	2A Chapter 9 Lesson 3	1B Chapter 13 Lesson 6

For Additional Support: See the Grade 3 Chapters 3 and 4 Math in Focus Background Videos on Think Central <www.k6.thinkcentral.com>.

Grade 2, Chapter 2

Students have learned...

BIG IDEA

Three-digit numbers can be added with and without regrouping.

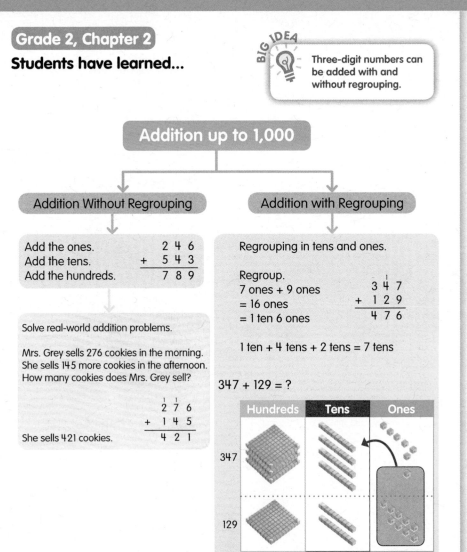

Addition up to 1,000

Addition Without Regrouping

Add the ones.
Add the tens.
Add the hundreds.

```
  2 4 6
+ 5 4 3
-------
  7 8 9
```

Solve real-world addition problems.

Mrs. Grey sells 276 cookies in the morning. She sells 145 more cookies in the afternoon. How many cookies does Mrs. Grey sell?

```
  1 1
  2 7 6
+ 1 4 5
-------
  4 2 1
```

She sells 421 cookies.

Addition with Regrouping

Regrouping in tens and ones.

Regroup.
7 ones + 9 ones
= 16 ones
= 1 ten 6 ones

```
  3 4¹ 7
+ 1 2 9
-------
  4 7 6
```

1 ten + 4 tens + 2 tens = 7 tens

347 + 129 = ?

Hundreds	Tens	Ones
347		
129		

Overview:

- In Grade 1, students learn to add up to two-digit numbers with and without regrouping.

- Addition of three-digit numbers is first shown with place-value blocks on a place-value mat.

- The concrete representation of the sum is then shown beside the steps of the algorithm.

- The skills are applied to solving real-world problems.

- Provide students hands-on experience using place-value blocks to add up to 1,000 with regrouping.

Grade 2, Chapter 3
Students have learned...

BIG IDEA
Subtract up to three-digit numbers with and without regrouping.

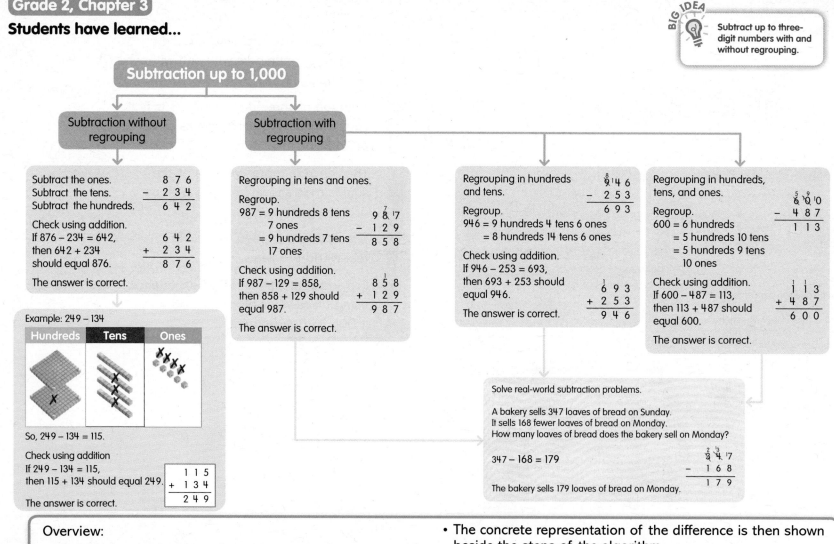

Subtraction up to 1,000

Subtraction without regrouping

Subtract the ones.
Subtract the tens.
Subtract the hundreds.

```
  8 7 6
-  2 3 4
  6 4 2
```

Check using addition.
If 876 – 234 = 642,
then 642 + 234
should equal 876.

```
  6 4 2
+  2 3 4
  8 7 6
```

The answer is correct.

Example: 249 – 134

Hundreds	Tens	Ones

So, 249 – 134 = 115.

Check using addition
If 249 – 134 = 115,
then 115 + 134 should equal 249.

```
  1 1 5
+ 1 3 4
  2 4 9
```

The answer is correct.

Subtraction with regrouping

Regrouping in tens and ones.

Regroup.
987 = 9 hundreds 8 tens
        7 ones
   = 9 hundreds 7 tens
        17 ones

```
  9 8⁷ ¹7
-   1 2 9
    8 5 8
```

Check using addition.
If 987 – 129 = 858,
then 858 + 129 should
equal 987.

```
  8 5⁸ 8
+   1 2 9
    9 8 7
```

The answer is correct.

Regrouping in hundreds and tens.

```
  ⁸9¹4 6
-   2 5 3
    6 9 3
```

Regroup.
946 = 9 hundreds 4 tens 6 ones
   = 8 hundreds 14 tens 6 ones

Check using addition.
If 946 – 253 = 693,
then 693 + 253 should
equal 946.

```
  6 9 3
+ 2 5 3
  9 4 6
```

The answer is correct.

Regrouping in hundreds, tens, and ones.

```
  ⁵6 ⁹0 ¹0
-   4 8 7
    1 1 3
```

Regroup.
600 = 6 hundreds
   = 5 hundreds 10 tens
   = 5 hundreds 9 tens
        10 ones

Check using addition.
If 600 – 487 = 113,
then 113 + 487 should
equal 600.

```
  ¹1 ¹1 3
+ 4 8 7
  6 0 0
```

The answer is correct.

Solve real-world subtraction problems.

A bakery sells 347 loaves of bread on Sunday.
It sells 168 fewer loaves of bread on Monday.
How many loaves of bread does the bakery sell on Monday?

347 – 168 = 179

```
  ²3 ¹³4 ¹7
-   1 6 8
    1 7 9
```

The bakery sells 179 loaves of bread on Monday.

Overview:

- In Grade 1, children subtract up to two-digit numbers, with and without regrouping.

- In Grade 2, subtraction of three-digit numbers is introduced, first with place-value blocks on a place-value mat.

- The concrete representation of the difference is then shown beside the steps of the algorithm.

- Students are encouraged to check all their work using inverse operations.

- These skills are applied to solving real-world problems in which children choose whether to add or subtract.

Grade 4: Chapter 2

Chapter 2: Estimation and Number Theory

Transition Topic: Mental Math

Grade 4 Chapter 2 Pre-Test Items	Grade 4 Chapter 2 Pre-Test Item Objective	Additional Support for the Objective: Grade 3 Reteach	Additional Support for the Objective: Grade 3 Extra Practice	Grade 3 Teacher Edition Support	Going Back Further (Grade 2)
	Add and subtract two-digit numbers mentally with or without regrouping.	3A pp. 17–30; See also 1A pp. 21–30; 33–35	Lessons 2.1–2.3; See also Grade 1 Lesson 2.1	3A Chapter 2 Lesson 3	2B Chapter 10 Lessons 2 and 4
Items 1; 3; 6–9; 16–17	Round numbers to estimate sums and differences.	3A pp. 31–38	Lesson 2.4	3A Chapter 2 Lesson 4	2B Chapter 10 Lesson 5
Items 2; 4; 10–11	Use front-end estimation to estimate sums and differences.	3A pp. 39–40	Lesson 2.5	3A Chapter 2 Lesson 5	2B Chapter 10 Lessons 2 and 4 (informal)

For Additional Support: See the Grade 4 Chapter 2 Math in Focus Background Videos on Think Central <www-k6.thinkcentral.com>.

Grade 3, Chapter 3

Students have learned...

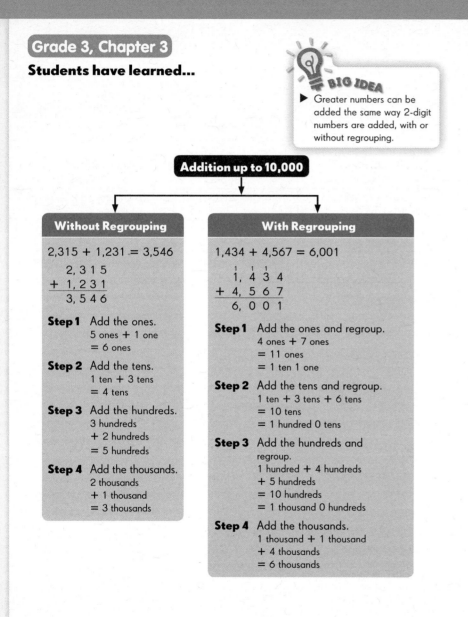

BIG IDEA

▶ Greater numbers can be added the same way 2-digit numbers are added, with or without regrouping.

Addition up to 10,000

Without Regrouping

$2,315 + 1,231 = 3,546$

```
  2, 3 1 5
+ 1, 2 3 1
---------
  3, 5 4 6
```

Step 1 Add the ones.
5 ones + 1 one
= 6 ones

Step 2 Add the tens.
1 ten + 3 tens
= 4 tens

Step 3 Add the hundreds.
3 hundreds
+ 2 hundreds
= 5 hundreds

Step 4 Add the thousands.
2 thousands
+ 1 thousand
= 3 thousands

With Regrouping

$1,434 + 4,567 = 6,001$

```
    1  1  1
  1, 4 3 4
+ 4, 5 6 7
---------
  6, 0 0 1
```

Step 1 Add the ones and regroup.
4 ones + 7 ones
= 11 ones
= 1 ten 1 one

Step 2 Add the tens and regroup.
1 ten + 3 tens + 6 tens
= 10 tens
= 1 hundred 0 tens

Step 3 Add the hundreds and regroup.
1 hundred + 4 hundreds
+ 5 hundreds
= 10 hundreds
= 1 thousand 0 hundreds

Step 4 Add the thousands.
1 thousand + 1 thousand
+ 4 thousands
= 6 thousands

Overview:

• In Grade 2, children have developed fluency in adding multi-digit numbers using different methods.

• Now the term *sum* is introduced to identify the result when adding.

• Numbers are added first with place-value blocks and then using the algorithm. The sum does not exceed 10,000.

• Ones are regrouped as tens, tens are regrouped as hundreds, and hundreds are regrouped as thousands.

• Give students problems to practice adding up to 10,000 with and without regrouping.

Grade 3, Chapter 4

Students have learned...

💡 BIG IDEA
▶ Greater numbers can be subtracted with or without regrouping.

Subtraction up to 10,000

Without Regrouping

Subtract the ones.
Subtract the tens.
Subtract the hundreds.
Subtract the thousands.

$$\begin{array}{r} 4,663 \\ -\ 1,231 \\ \hline 3,432 \end{array}$$

Check using addition.
If 4,663 − 1,231
= 3,432, then 3,432 + 1,231 should equal 4,663.

$$\begin{array}{r} 3,432 \\ +\ 1,231 \\ \hline 4,663 \end{array}$$

With Regrouping

Regroup.
9,876
= 9 thousands 8 hundreds
  7 tens 6 ones
= 9 thousands 8 hundreds 6 tens
  16 ones
= 9 thousands 7 hundreds 16 tens 16 ones
= 8 thousands 17 hundreds 16 tens
  16 ones

$$\begin{array}{r} 8\ ^17^16\ 1 \\ 9,876 \\ -\ 7,877 \\ \hline 1,999 \end{array}$$

Check using addition.
If 9,876 − 7,877 = 1,999,
then 1,999 + 7,877
should equal 9,876.

$$\begin{array}{r} 1\ \ 1\ \ 1 \\ 1,999 \\ +\ 7,877 \\ \hline 9,876 \end{array}$$

Regroup.
5,000
= 5 thousands
= 4 thousands 10 hundreds
= 4 thousands 9 hundreds 10 tens
= 4 thousands 9 hundreds 9 tens
  10 ones

$$\begin{array}{r} 4\ 9\ 9 \\ 5,0\cancel{0}\cancel{0}0 \\ -\ 4,321 \\ \hline 679 \end{array}$$

Check using addition.
If 5,000 − 4,321 = 679,
then 679 + 4,321
should equal 5,000.

$$\begin{array}{r} 1\ \ 1\ \ 1 \\ 679 \\ +\ 4,321 \\ \hline 5,000 \end{array}$$

Overview:

- In Grade 2, children have developed fluency in subtracting multi-digit numbers using different methods.

- Now the term *difference* is introduced to identify the result when subtracting.

- Numbers within 10,000 are subtracted first with place-value blocks and then using the algorithm.

- Tens are regrouped as ones, hundreds are regrouped as tens, and thousands are regrouped as hundreds.

- Subtraction is checked with the inverse operation, addition.

- Give students a variety of problems to practice subtracting up to 10,000 and checking their answers using addition.

Multiplication and Division of Whole Numbers

Exploring equal groups leads up to multiplication and division concepts in Grade 2. The basic multiplication and division facts are modeled and committed to memory in Grades 2 and 3. Grades 3 and 4 focus on multiplying and dividing multi-digit numbers, using both place-value blocks and place-value chips to aid understanding.

Grade 1

Children use models and pictures to count equal sets and divide large sets into smaller sets of equal size. It is a concrete/pictorial approach, with no mention of the terms *multiplication* or *division* or the writing of number sentences.

Grade 2

Grade 2 begins with a concrete/pictorial approach to representing multiplication and division as equal groups, and then uses number sentences to summarize these representations. The terms *multiplication* and *division* are introduced, but *product* and *quotient* are not.

Early in the year children are introduced to strategies for learning the multiplication facts for 2, 5, and 10, such as using skip-counting or array models shown on dot paper. They learn that they can figure out difficult facts by breaking them up into two easier facts and then adding or subtracting. For example, if they are having difficulty with 2×8, they can think of it as first finding 2×10 and then subtracting 2×2. Because this strategy is presented using dot paper arrays, it is very accessible to young children.

Later in the year, children use the same strategies to learn the multiplication facts for 3 and 4.

Grade 3

Students begin the year learning more strategies and models that they can use to develop the facts for 6, 7, 8, and 9. These models include array models, area models, and number line models. Once students are well acquainted with the basic facts, they learn how to multiply and divide two- and three-digit numbers by a one-digit number. Each step of the process is modeled using place-value blocks and then represented with a step in the algorithm.

Grade 4

Multiplying and dividing multi-digit numbers by one-digit numbers are reviewed, this time using place-value chips as the model. Again each step of the process is first modeled using the chips and then represented with a step in the algorithm. Students use arrays to model multiplying one-digit by two-digit numbers. Then they use area models to multiply two-digit by two-digit numbers. In both cases, they connect the action to the standard algorithm. Once students are well acquainted with the algorithm, they learn to multiply a multi-digit number by a two-digit number. For example, 26×243 is broken down into the partial products 6×243 and 2 tens $\times$ 243, so that students are using the skills of single-digit multiplication twice.

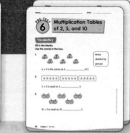

Grade 2: Chapters 5 and 6

Chapter 5: Multiplication and Division and
Chapter 6: Multiplication Tables of 2, 5, and 10

Transition Topic: Multiplication and Division of Whole Numbers

Grade 2 Chapters 5 and 6 Pre-Test Items	Grade 2 Chapters 5 and 6 Pre-Test Item Objective	Additional Support for the Objective: Grade 1 Reteach	Additional Support for the Objective: Grade 1 Extra Practice	Grade 1 Teacher Edition Support	Going Back Further (Grade K)
Chapter 5 Items 1–2, 4–6, 8–9	Relate repeated addition to the concept of multiplication.	1B, pp. 127–128	Lesson 18.1	1B Chapter 18 Lesson 1	
Chapter 5 Items 3, 10	Relate sharing equally to the concept of division.	1B, pp. 129–132	Lesson 18.2	1B Chapter 18 Lesson 2	
Chapter 6 Items 1, 4–7	Relate repeated addition to the concept of multiplication.	1B, pp. 127–128	Lesson 18.1	1B Chapter 18 Lesson 1	Kindergarten students count by twos in KB Chapter 8 Lesson 1
Chapter 6 Item 2	Use objects or pictures to find the total number of items in groups of the same size.	1B, pp. 129–132	Lesson 18.2	1B Chapter 18 Lesson 1	Kindergarten students count by twos in KB Chapter 8 Lesson 1
Chapter 6 Items 3, 11	Use objects or pictures to show the concept of division as finding the number of equal groups.	1B, pp. 133–136	Lesson 18.3	1B Chapter 18 Lesson 2	
Chapter 6 Items 8–10	Find the missing numbers in a number pattern.	1B, pp. 107–108	Lesson 16.3	1B Chapter 12 Lesson 3	

For Additional Support: See the Grade 2 Chapters 5 and 6 Math in Focus Background Videos on Think Central <www-k6.thinkcentral.com>.

Students have learned...

to add repeated numbers.

5 + 5 + 5 means 3 fives.
5 + 5 + 5 = 15
3 fives = 15

to use a picture with equal groups of things and write an addition sentence.

✱✱✱ ✱✱✱ ✱✱✱ ✱✱✱

3 + 3 + 3 + 3 = 12

to put or share things equally into groups.

Put 6 strawberries equally into 3 groups. How many strawberries are there in each group?

The number of groups is given.

There are 2 strawberries in each group.

BIG IDEAS

Multiplying is the same as adding equal groups. Dividing is the same as sharing things equally or putting things into equal groups.

to group things equally and find the number of groups.

Put 9 strawberries equally into groups of 3. How many groups of strawberries are there?

The number of things in each group is given.

There are 3 groups of strawberries.

Overview:

• This chapter explores equal groups in an informal way.

• The notation for multiplication and division is delayed until Grade 2.

• The terms *multiply*, *divide*, *product* and *quotient* are delayed until later grades, in keeping with the program's philosophy of using natural language to introduce concepts.

• Have children use concrete objects to model repeated addition and putting items in equal groups.

Instructional Pathway for Transition

Grade 3: Chapters 6, 7, and 8

Chapter 6: Multiplication Tables of 6, 7, 8, and 9; Chapter 7: Multiplication; and Chapter 8: Division

Transition Topic: Multiplication and Division of Whole Numbers

Grade 3 Chapters 6–8 Pre-Test Items	Grade 3 Chapters 6–8 Pre-Test Item Objective	Additional Support for the Objective: Grade 2 Reteach	Additional Support for the Objective: Grade 2 Extra Practice	Grade 2 Teacher Edition Support	Going Back Further (Grade 1)
Chapter 6 Items 1; 2; 4; 5	Use equal groups and repeated addition to multiply.	2A pp. 101–106	Lesson 5.1	2A Chapter 5 Lesson 1	1B Chapter 18 Lesson 1
Chapter 6 Items 3; 13	Divide to share equally.	2A pp. 107–109	Lesson 5.2	2A Chapter 5 Lesson 2	1B Chapter 18 Lesson 2
Chapter 6 Item 13	Solve division word problems.	2A p. 110–112	Lesson 5.3	2B Chapter 16 Lesson 3	1B Chapter 18 Lesson 2
Chapter 6 Item 4	Skip-count by 3s to multiply by 3.	2B pp. 91–92	Lesson 15.1	2B Chapter 15 Lesson 1	
Chapter 7 Items 1; 3	Use equal groups and repeated addition to multiply.	2A pp. 101–106	Lesson 5.1	2A Chapter 5 Lesson 1	1B Chapter 18 Lesson 1
Chapter 7 Item 2	Skip-count by 2s, 5s, and 10s.	2A pp. 115–118; 127–128; 133–134	Lessons 6.1; 6.3; 6.5	2A Chapter 6 Lesson 1 (× 2); Lesson 3 (× 5); Lesson 5 (× 10)	1B Chapter 19 Lesson 1
Chapter 7 Items 4–6	Identify related multiplication facts.	2A pp. 122–125; 131–132; 135–136	Lessons 6.2; 6.4; 6.5	2A Chapter 6 Lesson 2	
Chapter 7 Items 10–11	Solve multiplication word problems.	2A p. 113	Lesson 5.3	2B Chapter 16 Lesson 3	1B Chapter 18 Lesson 1
Chapter 7 Items 7–9	Use known multiplication facts to find new multiplication facts.	2A pp. 122–125		2A Chapter 6 Lesson 2	
	Use known multiplication facts to find new multiplication facts for 3.	2B pp. 98–99	Lesson 15.2	2B Chapter 15 Lesson 2	
	Use known multiplication facts to find new multiplication facts for 4.	2B pp. 106–107	Lesson 15.4	2B Chapter 15 Lesson 4	
Chapter 8 Items 1; 3	Divide by repeated subtraction of equal groups.	2A pp. 108–110	Lesson 5.2	2A Chapter 5 Lesson 2	1B Chapter 18 Lesson 2
Chapter 8 Item 2	Divide to share equally.	2A pp. 105–107	Lesson 5.2	2A Chapter 5 Lesson 3	1B Chapter 18 Lesson 2
Chapter 8 Item 4	Use related multiplication facts to find related division facts.	2B pp. 109–112	Lesson 6.6	2B Chapter 15 Lesson 5	
Chapter 8 Item 4	Find division facts using related multiplication facts.	2B pp. 109–112	Lesson 15.5	2B Chapter 15 Lesson 5	
Chapter 8 Items 10–11	Solve division word problems.	2A p. 114	Lesson 5.3	2B Chapter 16 Lesson 3	1B Chapter 18 Lesson 2

For Additional Support: See the Grade 3 Chapters 6–8 Math in Focus Background Videos on Think Central <www-k6.thinkcentral.com>.

BIG IDEA

Multiplication and division use equal groups.

Students have learned...

to use repeated addition or multiply to find the total number of things in equal groups.

There are 3 groups.	There are 5 △ in each group.
There are 5 △ in each group.	There are 3 groups.
$5 + 5 + 5 = 15$	$5 \times 3 = 5 + 5 + 5$
$3 \times 5 = 15$	$= 15$

to divide a given number of objects equally to find:

• the number of things in each group.

Divide 12 things into 3 equal groups.

$12 \div 3 = 4$

There are 4 things in each group.

• the number of groups.

Divide 12 things so there are 4 things in each group.

$12 \div 4 = 3$

There are 3 groups.

$12 - 4 - 4 - 4 = 0$ is the same as $12 \div 4 = 3$

groups of four are subtracted **3** times

to solve real-world problems with multiplication and division.

Overview:

• In preparation for solving problems involving multiplication and division, first-grade students have learned to skip count, add the same number repeatedly, and make equal groups.

• Multiplication and division are introduced as repeated addition and repeated subtraction of equal groups.

• Both interpretations of division are introduced: dividing a given number of things equally to find either the number of groups or the number of things in each group.

• The terms *multiply* and *divide* and the symbols × and ÷ are introduced.

• Using these core concepts of multiplication and division, children learn to solve real-world problems by first choosing whether to multiply or divide.

Grade 2, Chapter 6

Students have learned...

Multiplying 2, 5, and 10 using:

Skip-counting

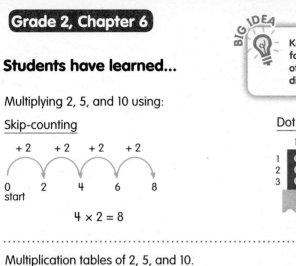

$4 \times 2 = 8$

Dot paper

$3 \times 5 = 15$

BIG IDEA
Known multiplication facts can be used to find other multiplication and division facts.

Multiplication tables of 2, 5, and 10.

1	×	2	=	2
2	×	2	=	4
3	×	2	=	6
4	×	2	=	8
5	×	2	=	10
6	×	2	=	12
7	×	2	=	14
8	×	2	=	16
9	×	2	=	18
10	×	2	=	20

1	×	5	=	5
2	×	5	=	10
3	×	5	=	15
4	×	5	=	20
5	×	5	=	25
6	×	5	=	30
7	×	5	=	35
8	×	5	=	40
9	×	5	=	45
10	×	5	=	50

1	×	10	=	10
2	×	10	=	20
3	×	10	=	30
4	×	10	=	40
5	×	10	=	50
6	×	10	=	60
7	×	10	=	70
8	×	10	=	80
9	×	10	=	90
10	×	10	=	100

to multiply numbers in any order.

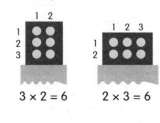
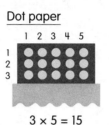

$3 \times 2 = 6$ $2 \times 3 = 6$

to use multiplication facts you know to find new multiplication facts.

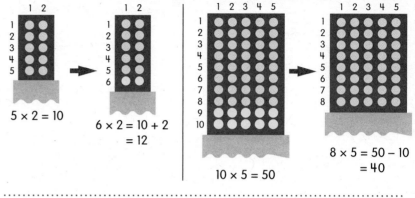

$5 \times 2 = 10$

$6 \times 2 = 10 + 2$
$= 12$

$10 \times 5 = 50$

$8 \times 5 = 50 - 10$
$= 40$

to divide using a related multiplication fact.

$20 \div 4 = 5$

$5 \times 4 = 20$
So, $20 \div 4 = 5$.

to write multiplication sentences and related division sentences.

$6 \times 2 = 12$ $3 \times 5 = 15$ $8 \times 10 = 80$
$2 \times 6 = 12$ $5 \times 3 = 15$ $10 \times 8 = 80$
So, $12 \div 2 = 6$ So, $15 \div 5 = 3$ So, $80 \div 10 = 8$
$12 \div 6 = 2$ $15 \div 3 = 5$ $80 \div 8 = 10$

to solve multiplication and division word problems.

Overview:

- The multiplication tables of 2, 5, and 10 are introduced through skip-counting. These facts are also connected to arrays through the use of dot paper models.

- The Commutative Property of Multiplication is introduced using the dot paper arrays.

- Facts for greater numbers are generated by recalling facts for nearby numbers and then adding or subtracting an appropriate amount, an informal use of the Distributive Property.

- Division facts are developed through recalling related multiplication facts.

Grade 2, Chapter 15

Students have learned...

BIG IDEA Known multiplication facts can be used to find other multiplication and division facts.

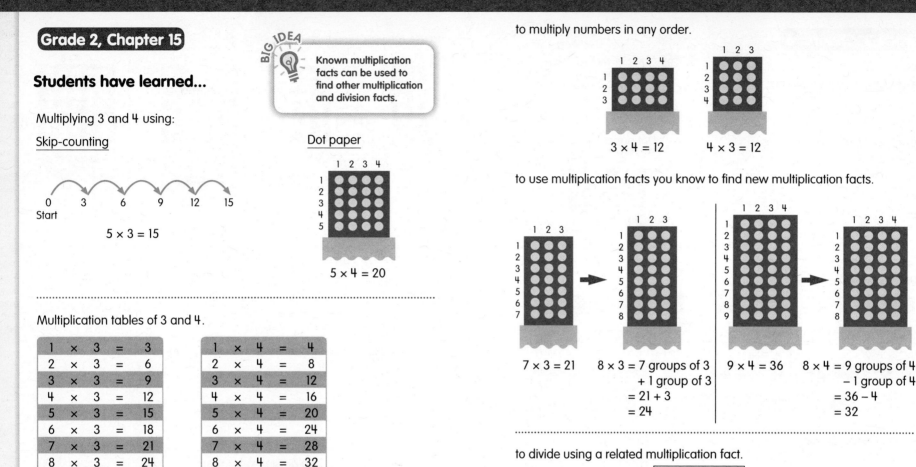

Multiplying 3 and 4 using:

Skip-counting

0   3   6   9   12   15
Start

$5 \times 3 = 15$

Dot paper

$5 \times 4 = 20$

Multiplication tables of 3 and 4.

1	×	3	=	3
2	×	3	=	6
3	×	3	=	9
4	×	3	=	12
5	×	3	=	15
6	×	3	=	18
7	×	3	=	21
8	×	3	=	24
9	×	3	=	27
10	×	3	=	30

1	×	4	=	4
2	×	4	=	8
3	×	4	=	12
4	×	4	=	16
5	×	4	=	20
6	×	4	=	24
7	×	4	=	28
8	×	4	=	32
9	×	4	=	36
10	×	4	=	40

to multiply numbers in any order.

$3 \times 4 = 12$ $4 \times 3 = 12$

to use multiplication facts you know to find new multiplication facts.

$7 \times 3 = 21$ $8 \times 3 = 7$ groups of 3
                       + 1 group of 3
                       = 21 + 3
                       = 24

$9 \times 4 = 36$ $8 \times 4 = 9$ groups of 4
                       − 1 group of 4
                       = 36 − 4
                       = 32

to divide using a related multiplication fact.

$32 \div 4 = 8$

$8 \times 4 = 32$
So, $32 \div 4 = 8$

Overview:

- The facts for 3 and 4 are developed through skip-counting and array models.

- Difficult facts are related to easier facts for nearby numbers (such as 5 and 10) and then adding or subtracting an appropriate amount.

- Give students hands-on experience using the dot-paper strategy, in which each column of dots represents the number of groups while each row of dots represents the number of items in each group.

Continued

to write multiplication sentences and related division sentences.

$8 \times 3 = 24$	$7 \times 4 = 28$
$3 \times 8 = 24$	$4 \times 7 = 28$
So, $24 \div 3 = 8$	So, $28 \div 4 = 7$
$24 \div 8 = 3$	$28 \div 7 = 4$

....

to solve multiplication and division word problems.

There are 8 tables in the classroom.
Each table has 4 chairs.
How many chairs are there in all?

$8 \times 4 = 32$

There are 32 chairs in all.

....

Mrs. Dempsey divides 40 pieces of craft paper equally
among her students.
She has 20 students.
How many pieces of craft paper does each student get?

$40 \div 20 = 2$

Each students gets 2 pieces of craft paper.

Overview:

• In Grade 1, children learned to add equal groups to multiply.

• Now they learn that they can take away equal groups to divide.

• Division facts are developed through recalling related multiplication facts.

• Children solve real-world problems by first choosing whether to multiply or divide.

• Give students the opportunity to use manipulatives to model equal groups.

Grade 4: Chapter 3

Chapter 3: Whole Number Multiplication and Division

Transition Topic: Multiplication and Division of Whole Numbers

Grade 4 Chapter 3 Pre-Test Items	Grade 4 Chapter 3 Pre-Test Item Objective	Additional Support for the Objective: Grade 3 Reteach	Additional Support for the Objective: Grade 3 Extra Practice	Grade 3 Teacher Edition Support	Going Back Further (Grade 2)
Items 5–6	Understand multiplication by using array models.	3A pp. 91–114	Lesson 6.2	3A Chapter 6 Lesson 5	2B Chapter 15 Lesson 4
	Understand multiplication by using area models.		Lesson 6.3	3A Chapter 6 Lesson 3	
Item 1	Understand multiplication by using number lines.	3A pp. 79–82	Lesson 6.1	3A Chapter 6 Lesson 1	2B Chapter 16 Lesson 1
Item 9	Multiply by ones, tens, and hundreds mentally.	3A pp. 123–128	Lesson 7.1	3A Chapter 7 Lesson 1	
Items 4; 9–10	Multiply ones, tens, and hundreds with regrouping.	3A pp. 133–140	Lesson 7.3	3A Chapter 7 Lesson 3	
	Use patterns to divide multiples of 10 and 100.	3A pp. 142–144	Lesson 8.1	3A Chapter 8 Lesson 1	
Item 12	Divide numbers by a one-digit number without remainder or regrouping.	3A pp. 145; 149; 153–156	Lesson 8.3	3A Chapter 8 Lesson 4	2B Chapter 16 Lesson 2 (using bar models)
Items 3; 11	Divide numbers by a one-digit number with remainder or regrouping.	3A pp. 146–148; 157–162	Lesson 8.2	3A Chapter 8 Lesson 5	
Item 15	Solve real-world problems involving division.		Lesson 8.4	3A Chapter 9 Lesson 4	

For Additional Support: See the Grade 4 Chapter 3 Math in Focus Background Videos on Think Central <www-k6.thinkcentral.com>.

Multiplication and Division of Whole Numbers

Grade 3, Chapter 6

Students have learned...

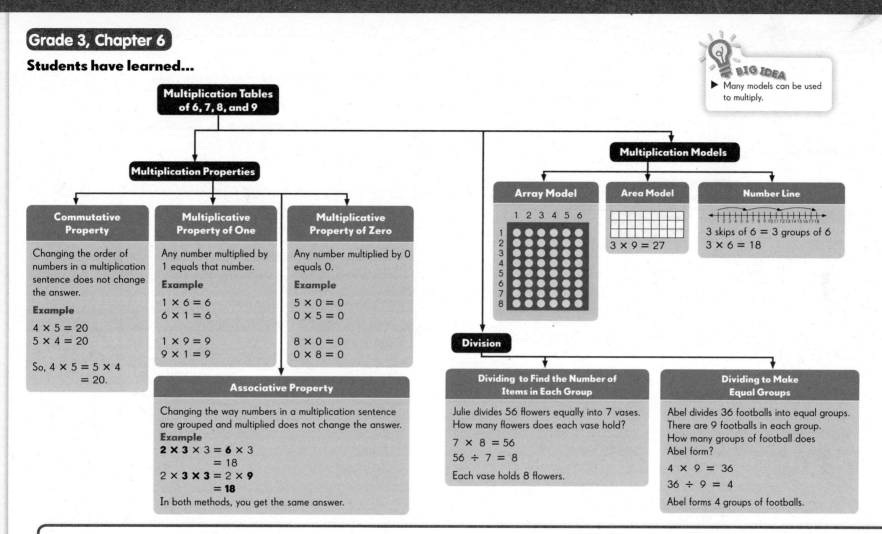

🔦 **BIG IDEA**
► Many models can be used to multiply.

Multiplication Tables of 6, 7, 8, and 9

Multiplication Properties

Commutative Property

Changing the order of numbers in a multiplication sentence does not change the answer.

Example

$4 \times 5 = 20$
$5 \times 4 = 20$

So, $4 \times 5 = 5 \times 4$
    $= 20$.

Multiplicative Property of One

Any number multiplied by 1 equals that number.

Example

$1 \times 6 = 6$
$6 \times 1 = 6$

$1 \times 9 = 9$
$9 \times 1 = 9$

Multiplicative Property of Zero

Any number multiplied by 0 equals 0.

Example

$5 \times 0 = 0$
$0 \times 5 = 0$

$8 \times 0 = 0$
$0 \times 8 = 0$

Associative Property

Changing the way numbers in a multiplication sentence are grouped and multiplied does not change the answer.

Example

$2 \times 3 \times 3 = 6 \times 3$
$\qquad\qquad = 18$
$2 \times 3 \times 3 = 2 \times 9$
$\qquad\qquad = 18$

In both methods, you get the same answer.

Multiplication Models

Array Model

1 2 3 4 5 6

Area Model

$3 \times 9 = 27$

Number Line

3 skips of 6 = 3 groups of 6
$3 \times 6 = 18$

Division

Dividing to Find the Number of Items in Each Group

Julie divides 56 flowers equally into 7 vases. How many flowers does each vase hold?

$7 \times 8 = 56$
$56 \div 7 = 8$

Each vase holds 8 flowers.

Dividing to Make Equal Groups

Abel divides 36 footballs into equal groups. There are 9 footballs in each group. How many groups of football does Abel form?

$4 \times 9 = 36$
$36 \div 9 = 4$

Abel forms 4 groups of footballs.

Overview:

- Properties of multiplication are formally introduced. Help students see the similarities to addition properties learned in first and second grade.
- Students develop the facts of 6, 7, 8, and 9 through array models, area models, and number line models.

- Difficult multiplication facts are related to easier facts for nearby numbers (such as 5 and 10) and then adding or subtracting an appropriate amount.
- Division facts are developed through recalling related multiplication facts.
- Real-world division problems may involve finding either the number of equal groups or the number of items in each equal group.

Multiplication and Division of Whole Numbers

BIG IDEAS

▶ Mental math can be used to multiply.
▶ Numbers up to 3-digits can be multiplied with or without regrouping.

Students have learned...

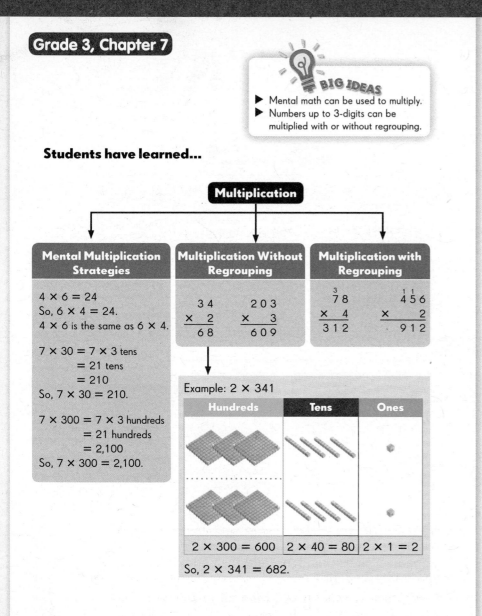

Mental Multiplication Strategies	Multiplication Without Regrouping	Multiplication with Regrouping

Mental Multiplication Strategies

4 × 6 = 24
So, 6 × 4 = 24.
4 × 6 is the same as 6 × 4.

7 × 30 = 7 × 3 tens
　　　 = 21 tens
　　　 = 210
So, 7 × 30 = 210.

7 × 300 = 7 × 3 hundreds
　　　　 = 21 hundreds
　　　　 = 2,100
So, 7 × 300 = 2,100.

Multiplication Without Regrouping

```
  3 4          2 0 3
×   2        ×     3
-----        -------
  6 8          6 0 9
```

Example: 2 × 341

Hundreds	Tens	Ones
2 × 300 = 600	2 × 40 = 80	2 × 1 = 2

So, 2 × 341 = 682.

Multiplication with Regrouping

```
   3
   7 8          4 5 6
×    4        ×     2
-----        -------
 3 1 2          9 1 2
```

Overview:

- Students count by 10s, and make the connection to multiplying by 10.

- Multiplication by multiples of 10 and 100 is introduced, as well as the term *product*.

- Multiplying a multi-digit number by a one-digit number is modeled using place-value blocks.

- The algorithm develops from recording the steps used for modeling the product.

- Problems that involve both regrouping and no regrouping are included.

- Students get hands-on practice using place-value models to multiply multi-digit numbers by one-digit numbers.

Multiplication and Division of Whole Numbers

Grade 3, Chapter 8

Students have learned...

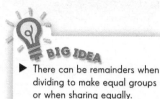

BIG IDEA

▶ There can be remainders when dividing to make equal groups or when sharing equally.

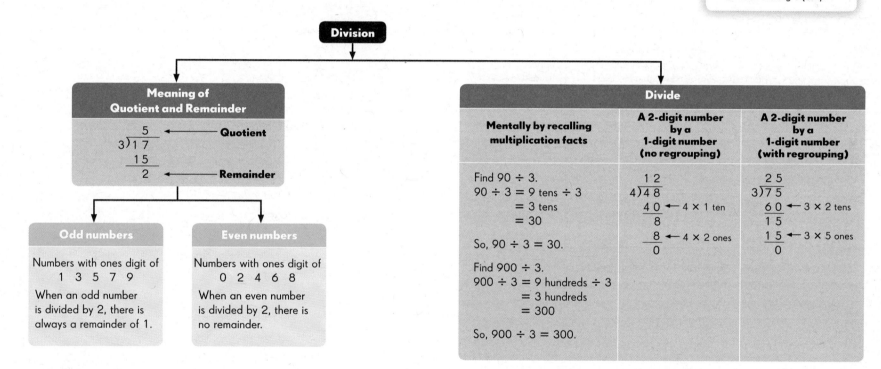

Division

Meaning of Quotient and Remainder

$$3\overline{)17}$$

5 ← Quotient

15

2 ← Remainder

Odd numbers

Numbers with ones digit of
1 3 5 7 9

When an odd number is divided by 2, there is always a remainder of 1.

Even numbers

Numbers with ones digit of
0 2 4 6 8

When an even number is divided by 2, there is no remainder.

Divide

Mentally by recalling multiplication facts	A 2-digit number by a 1-digit number (no regrouping)	A 2-digit number by a 1-digit number (with regrouping)

Find 90 ÷ 3.
90 ÷ 3 = 9 tens ÷ 3
       = 3 tens
       = 30
 	
So, 90 ÷ 3 = 30.
 	
Find 900 ÷ 3.
900 ÷ 3 = 9 hundreds ÷ 3
        = 3 hundreds
        = 300
 	
So, 900 ÷ 3 = 300.
	12
	4)48
	40 ← 4 × 1 ten
	8
	8 ← 4 × 2 ones
	0
		25
		3)75
		60 ← 3 × 2 tens
		15
		15 ← 3 × 5 ones
		0

Overview:

• Division with a remainder is introduced by modeling repeated subtraction with some left over that cannot be made into an equal group. The terms *quotient* and *remainder* are used.

• Odd and even numbers are used to help students understand what a remainder is. Students can now understand the properties "having no remainder" and "having a remainder of 1."

• Division of a two-digit number by a one-digit number is modeled step by step using place-value blocks, with the corresponding steps to the algorithm beside each modeled step.

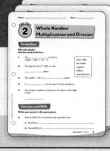

Grade 5: Chapter 2

Chapter 2: Whole Number Multiplication and Division

Transition Topic: Multiplication and Division of Whole Numbers

Grade 5 Chapter 2 Pre-Test Items	Grade 5 Chapter 2 Pre-Test Item Objective	Additional Support for the Objective: Grade 4 Reteach	Additional Support for the Objective: Grade 4 Extra Practice	Grade 4 Teacher Edition Support	Going Back Further (Grade 3)
Items 1, 6	Write numbers to 100,000 in standard form, word form, and expanded form.	Support for this objective is included in Chapter 1.		4A Chapter 1 Lesson 1	Grade 3 students write numbers to 10,000 in 3A Chapter 1 Lesson 2
Items 2, 3, 14–19	Estimate products and quotients.	Support for this objective is included in Chapter 1.		4A Chapter 2 Lesson 1	
Items 5, 12	Round numbers to estimate sums, differences, products, and quotients. Estimate to check that an answer is reasonable.	Support for this objective is included in Chapter 1.		4A Chapter 2 Lesson 1	Grade 3 students estimate sums and differences in 3A Chapter 2 Lesson 4
Item 9	Use different methods to multiply whole numbers up to 4-digits by one-digit and two-digit numbers with or without regrouping.	4A pp. 49–63	Lessons 3.1 and 3.2	4A Chapter 3 Lessons 1 and 2	Grade 3 students multiply with ones, tens, and hundreds in 3A Chapter 7 Lessons 1 and 3
Items 10–11	Divide up to a 4-digit number by a one-digit number with regrouping, and with or without remainders.	4A pp. 69–77	Lessons 3.3 and 3.4	4A Chapter 3 Lesson 4	Grade 3 students divide numbers by a one-digit number without regrouping or remainders in 3A Chapter 8 Lesson 4

For Additional Support: See the Grade 5 Chapter 2 Math in Focus Background Videos on Think Central <www-k6.thinkcentral.com>.

Grade 4, Chapter 3

Students have learned...

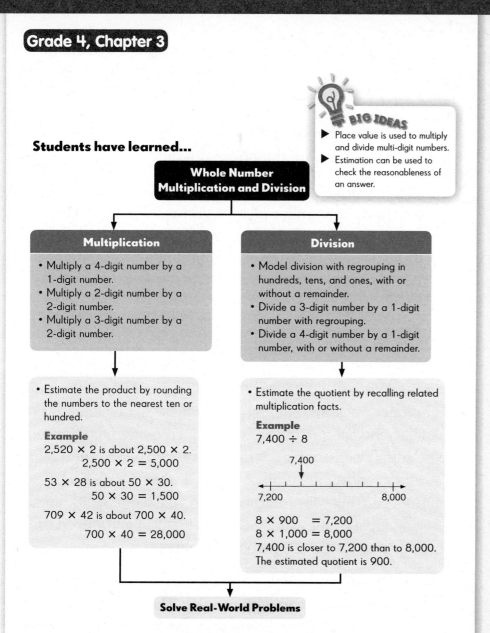

BIG IDEAS
▶ Place value is used to multiply and divide multi-digit numbers.
▶ Estimation can be used to check the reasonableness of an answer.

Whole Number Multiplication and Division

Multiplication
- Multiply a 4-digit number by a 1-digit number.
- Multiply a 2-digit number by a 2-digit number.
- Multiply a 3-digit number by a 2-digit number.

- Estimate the product by rounding the numbers to the nearest ten or hundred.

Example
2,520 × 2 is about 2,500 × 2.
2,500 × 2 = 5,000

53 × 28 is about 50 × 30.
50 × 30 = 1,500

709 × 42 is about 700 × 40.
700 × 40 = 28,000

Division
- Model division with regrouping in hundreds, tens, and ones, with or without a remainder.
- Divide a 3-digit number by a 1-digit number with regrouping.
- Divide a 4-digit number by a 1-digit number, with or without a remainder.

- Estimate the quotient by recalling related multiplication facts.

Example
7,400 ÷ 8

7,400
↓

7,200   8,000

8 × 900   = 7,200
8 × 1,000 = 8,000
7,400 is closer to 7,200 than to 8,000.
The estimated quotient is 900.

Solve Real-World Problems

Overview:

- In earlier grades students learned the multiplication tables, which should be reviewed to facilitate multiplication and division with multi-digit numbers.

- Students multiply multi-digit numbers by one-digit numbers using place-value chips and array models.

- Students multiply multi-digit numbers by two-digit numbers using area models.

- Students divide multi-digit numbers by one-digit numbers, modeling each step with place-value chips.

- The standard algorithms arise from recording each step illustrated by the models.

- Multiplying by a two-digit number such as 63 is done by breaking the 63 into 6 tens and 3 ones, and applying single-digit multiplication to find the partial products.

- Once the division algorithm is established, students learn about remainders—what they are and how to record them.

- Answers are checked for reasonableness by estimating the products or quotients.

Fractions and Mixed Numbers

Fraction concepts are introduced gradually, with abundant pictorial support. Understanding grows from fractions of a whole (with an emphasis on unit fractions) to fractions of a set and comparing fractions to addition and subtraction of like and unlike fractions.

Grade 2

Children are introduced to fractions for the first time. They learn to describe equal parts of a whole as fractions, to write fractions, and to compare fractions (halves, thirds, and fourths only). To aid students in visualization before moving to the abstract level, geometric models are used to model equal parts of a whole. Children are also taught to add and subtract like fractions, again using only halves, thirds, and fourths.

Grade 3

Students work with unit fractions, building a whole from unit fractions, then comparing and ordering unit fractions with different denominators. They then compare non-unit fractions with the same denominator. They use the key terms *numerator* and *denominator*. They develop an understanding of the meanings and uses of fractions to represent whole numbers, equal parts of a whole or a set, and points or distances on number lines and rulers.

Models such as fraction strips, fraction circles, and number lines are used to illustrate adding and subtracting like fractions. Area models help students to visualize equivalent fractions before students learn to multiply numerators and

denominators by the same number. Equivalent fractions are used to compare fractions with unlike denominators.

Students learn to read, write, and identify fractions of a set and to find the number of items represented by a fraction of a set. Pictorial models illustrate real-world problems before information is translated into number sentences.

Grade 4

The focus of the work with fractions in Grade 4 is on comparing fractions to benchmarks and to each other and on understanding and converting between mixed numbers and improper fractions. Students apply these understandings to adding and subtracting fractions that require renaming either the sum (when adding) or the subtrahend (when subtracting). Addition and subtraction of unlike fractions is also introduced, but only for fractions in which one denominator is a multiple of the other. Students are also introduced to multiplying fractions by whole numbers.

Throughout the work with fractions, concepts are continually reinforced with models. They may be fraction circles, fraction strips, or number line models, depending on the concept under consideration.

Grade 3: Chapter 14

Chapter 14: Fractions

Transition Topic: Fractions

Grade 3 Chapter 14 Pre-Test Items	Grade 3 Chapter 14 Pre-Test Item Objective	Additional Support for the Objective: Grade 2 Reteach	Additional Support for the Objective: Grade 2 Extra Practice	Grade 2 Teacher Edition Support	Going Back Further (Grade 1)
Items 1; 3	Read, write, and identify unit fractions for halves, thirds, and fourths.	2B p. 52	Lesson 12.1	2B Chapter 12 Lesson 1	
Items 1; 3	Show fractions and a whole using model drawings.	2B pp. 51–52	Lesson 12.1	2B Chapter 12 Lesson 1	
Items 4; 5–7	Compare and order two or more unit fractions with or without the use of models.	2B pp. 55–56	Lesson 12.2	2B Chapter 12 Lesson 2	
Items 2; 8	Add and subtract like fractions with or without the use of models.	2B pp. 57–60	Lesson 12.3	2B Chapter 12 Lesson 3	

For Additional Support: See the Grade 3 Chapter 14 Math in Focus Background Videos on Think Central <www-k6.thinkcentral.com>.

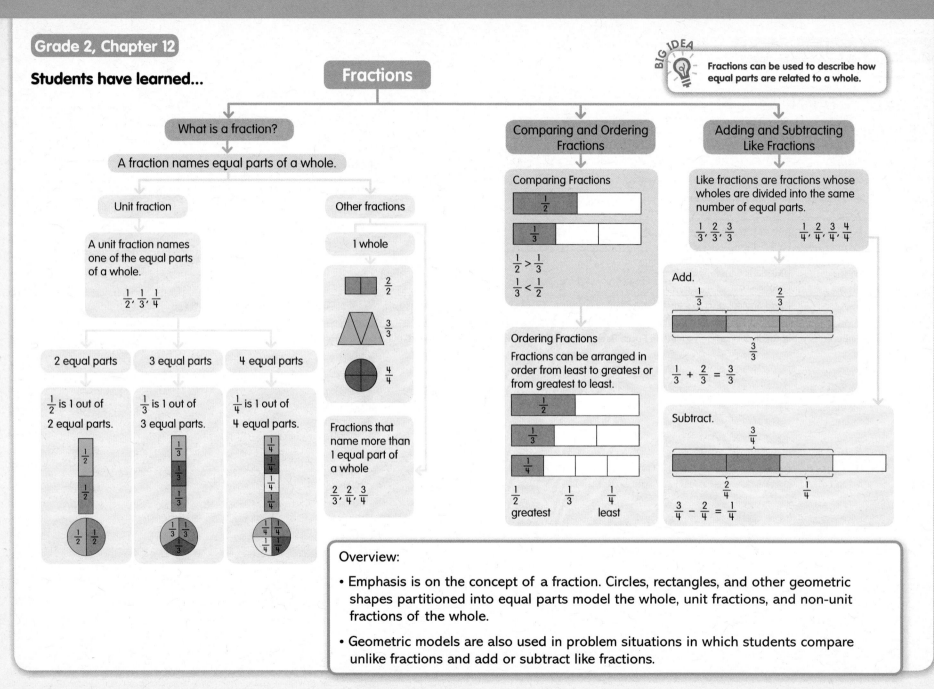

Grade 2, Chapter 12

Students have learned...

Fractions

BIG IDEA — Fractions can be used to describe how equal parts are related to a whole.

What is a fraction?

A fraction names equal parts of a whole.

Unit fraction

A unit fraction names one of the equal parts of a whole.

$\frac{1}{2}$, $\frac{1}{3}$, $\frac{1}{4}$

2 equal parts

$\frac{1}{2}$ is 1 out of 2 equal parts.

$\frac{1}{2}$ $\frac{1}{2}$

$\frac{1}{2}$ $\frac{1}{2}$

3 equal parts

$\frac{1}{3}$ is 1 out of 3 equal parts.

$\frac{1}{3}$ $\frac{1}{3}$ $\frac{1}{3}$

$\frac{1}{3}$ $\frac{1}{3}$ $\frac{1}{3}$

4 equal parts

$\frac{1}{4}$ is 1 out of 4 equal parts.

$\frac{1}{4}$ $\frac{1}{4}$ $\frac{1}{4}$ $\frac{1}{4}$

$\frac{1}{4}$ $\frac{1}{4}$ $\frac{1}{4}$ $\frac{1}{4}$

Other fractions

1 whole

$\frac{2}{2}$

$\frac{3}{3}$

$\frac{4}{4}$

Fractions that name more than 1 equal part of a whole

$\frac{2}{3}$, $\frac{2}{4}$, $\frac{3}{4}$

Comparing and Ordering Fractions

Comparing Fractions

$\frac{1}{2}$

$\frac{1}{3}$

$\frac{1}{2} > \frac{1}{3}$

$\frac{1}{3} < \frac{1}{2}$

Ordering Fractions

Fractions can be arranged in order from least to greatest or from greatest to least.

$\frac{1}{2}$

$\frac{1}{3}$

$\frac{1}{4}$

$\frac{1}{2}$ $\frac{1}{3}$ $\frac{1}{4}$

greatest   least

Adding and Subtracting Like Fractions

Like fractions are fractions whose wholes are divided into the same number of equal parts.

$\frac{1}{3}$, $\frac{2}{3}$, $\frac{3}{3}$ $\frac{1}{4}$, $\frac{2}{4}$, $\frac{3}{4}$, $\frac{4}{4}$

Add.

$\frac{1}{3}$ $\frac{2}{3}$

$\frac{3}{3}$

$\frac{1}{3} + \frac{2}{3} = \frac{3}{3}$

Subtract.

$\frac{3}{4}$

$\frac{2}{4}$ $\frac{1}{4}$

$\frac{3}{4} - \frac{2}{4} = \frac{1}{4}$

Overview:

• Emphasis is on the concept of a fraction. Circles, rectangles, and other geometric shapes partitioned into equal parts model the whole, unit fractions, and non-unit fractions of the whole.

• Geometric models are also used in problem situations in which students compare unlike fractions and add or subtract like fractions.

Grade 4: Chapter 6

Chapter 6: Fractions and Mixed Numbers

Transition Topic: Fractions

Grade 4 Chapter 6 Pre-Test Items	Grade 4 Chapter 6 Pre-Test Item Objective	Additional Support for the Objective: Grade 3 Reteach	Additional Support for the Objective: Grade 3 Extra Practice	Grade 3 Teacher Edition Support	Going Back Further (Grade 2)
Item 3	Use models to identify equivalent fractions.	3B pp. 85–87	Lesson 14.2	3B Chapter 14 Lesson 1	2B Chapter 12 Lesson 1
Items 3; 5	Use a number line to identify equivalent fractions.	3B p. 88	Lesson 14.2	3B Chapter 14 Lesson 2	
Item 3	Use multiplication and division to find equivalent fractions.	3B pp. 89–96	Lesson 14.3	3B Chapter 14 Lesson 3	
Items 2; 6; 7	Write fractions in simplest form.	3B pp. 92–96	Lesson 14.3	3B Chapter 14 Lesson 3	
	Compare and order fractions.	3B pp. 97–106	Lesson 14.4	3B Chapter 14 Lesson 4	Grade 2 students compare and order unit fractions in 2B Chapter 12 Lesson 2
Items 1; 7; 10	Add two or three like fractions with sums of 1.	3B pp. 107–110		3B Chapter 14 Lesson 5	2B Chapter 12 Lesson 3
Items 1; 7; 11	Subtract a like fraction from another like fraction or one whole.	3B pp. 110–112		3B Chapter 14 Lesson 5	2B Chapter 12 Lesson 3
Item 8	Read, write, and identify fractions of a set.	3B pp. 113–114	Lesson 14.5	3B Chapter 14 Lesson 6	
Items 4; 9	Find the number of items in a fraction of a set.	3B pp. 115–116	Lesson 14.5	3B Chapter 14 Lesson 6	

For Additional Support: See the Grade 4 Chapter 6 Math in Focus Background Videos on Think Central <www-k6.thinkcentral.com>.

Fractions and Mixed Numbers

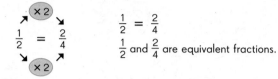

BIG IDEA

► Fractions can be used to describe parts of a region or parts of a set.

Students have learned...

Understanding fractions, numerator, and denominator:

Unit fractions

$\frac{1}{6}$ is one-sixth.　　　$\frac{1}{7}$ is one-seventh.　　　$\frac{1}{8}$ is one-eighth.

$\frac{1}{9}$ is one-ninth.　　　$\frac{1}{10}$ is one-tenth.　　　$\frac{1}{11}$ is one-eleventh.

$\frac{1}{12}$ is one-twelfth.

Identifying fractions to make a whole

$\frac{2}{5}$ and $\frac{3}{5}$ make 1 whole.

Numerator and Denominator

$\frac{2}{4}$ ← Numerator: The number of equal parts shaded.
　← Denominator: The number of equal parts the whole is divided into.

Equivalent fractions:

Using a model

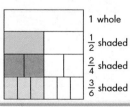

1 whole
$\frac{1}{2}$ shaded
$\frac{2}{4}$ shaded
$\frac{3}{6}$ shaded

Using a number line

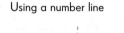

0　　　$\frac{1}{2}$　　　1

0　$\frac{1}{4}$　$\frac{2}{4}$　$\frac{3}{4}$　1

Overview:

- Whole numbers are expressed in fraction form.
- Equivalent fractions are formed by multiplying or dividing the numerator and denominator of a fraction by the same number.
- Like and unlike fractions are compared and ordered.

Using multiplication and division:

×2
$\frac{1}{2} = \frac{2}{4}$
×2

$\frac{1}{2} = \frac{2}{4}$

$\frac{1}{2}$ and $\frac{2}{4}$ are equivalent fractions.

Comparing and ordering fractions:

Like fractions are fractions with the same denominators and unlike fractions are fractions with different denominators.

Comparing like fractions

$\frac{3}{7}$　　　$\frac{5}{7}$ is the greatest.

$\frac{5}{7}$　　　$\frac{1}{7}$ is the least.

$\frac{1}{7}$　　　$\frac{5}{7}$, $\frac{3}{7}$, $\frac{1}{7}$
　　　greatest

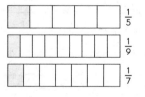

When the denominators are the same, compare the numerators.

Comparing unlike fractions with the same numerator

$\frac{1}{5}$　　$\frac{1}{9}$ is less than $\frac{1}{7}$.

$\frac{1}{9}$　　$\frac{1}{5}$ is greater than $\frac{1}{9}$.

$\frac{1}{7}$　　$\frac{1}{5}$, $\frac{1}{7}$, $\frac{1}{9}$
　　　greatest

Using multiplication and division to compare

×2
$\frac{1}{3} = \frac{2}{6}$　$\frac{1}{3}$ is less than $\frac{5}{6}$.
×2

÷3
$\frac{6}{12} = \frac{2}{4}$　$\frac{6}{12}$ is less than $\frac{3}{4}$.
÷3

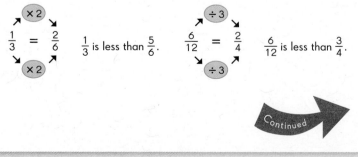

Continued

Fractions and Mixed Numbers

Using number lines and a benchmark of $\frac{1}{2}$

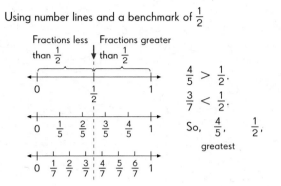

$\frac{4}{5} > \frac{1}{2}$.

$\frac{3}{7} < \frac{1}{2}$.

So, $\frac{4}{5}$, $\frac{1}{2}$, $\frac{3}{7}$.

greatest

Adding and subtracting like fractions:

$\frac{1}{7} + \frac{5}{7} = \frac{6}{7}$

$\frac{6}{7} - \frac{2}{7} = \frac{4}{7}$

Finding fractions of a set using models

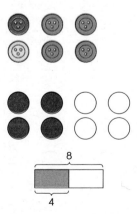

$\frac{4}{6}$ of the buttons are blue.

$\frac{2}{6}$ of the buttons are not blue.

$\frac{6}{6}$ of the buttons are round.

$\frac{1}{2}$ of the set of circles is red.

$\frac{1}{2}$ of 8 is 4.

$\frac{1}{2}$ of the bar model is shaded.

$\frac{1}{2}$ of 8 is 4.

Overview:

• In Grade 2, an understanding of fractions is built by connecting geometric concepts with unit fractions.

• In Grade 3, benchmarks are used to order and compare fractions.

• Adding and subtracting like fractions are developed pictorially and intuitively and proceed to solving without models.

• The concept of a fraction is extended to fraction of a set, which is taught pictorially.

• Exposure to real-world problems helps students to make sense of what they have learned in everyday situations.

• Students are given opportunities to work with different types of models (bar models, number lines, sets of items) to show fraction concepts.

Instructional Pathway for Transition

Grade 5: Chapters 3 and 4

Chapter 3: Fractions and Mixed Numbers and
Chapter 4: Multiplying and Dividing Fractions and Mixed Numbers

Transition Topic: Number and Operations: Fractions

Grade 5 Chapters 3–4 Pre-Test Items	Grade 5 Chapters 3–4 Pre-Test Item Objective	Additional Support for the Objective: Grade 4 Reteach	Additional Support for the Objective: Grade 4 Extra Practice	Grade 4 Teacher Edition Support	Going Back Further (Grade 3)
Chapter 3 Items 1–7, 8–10	Find equivalent fractions.	4A pp. 151–157, 159, 162–163	Lesson 6.1	4A Chapter 6 Lesson 1	3B Chapter 14 Lesson 3
Chapter 3 Items 12–13	Add unlike fractions.	4A pp. 153–155, 157–158	Lesson 6.1	4A Chapter 6 Lesson 1	Grade 3 students add and subtract like fractions in Chapter 14 Lesson 3
Chapter 3 Items 14–15	Subtract unlike fractions.	4A pp. 160–166	Lesson 6.2	4A Chapter 6 Lesson 2	Grade 3 students add and subtract like fractions in Chapter 14 Lesson 3
	Write a mixed number for a model.	4A pp. 167–170	Lesson 6.3	4A Chapter 6 Lesson 3	
	Draw models to represent mixed numbers.	4A pp. 167, 169	Lesson 6.3	4A Chapter 6 Lesson 3	
	Write an improper fraction for a model.	4A pp. 171–176	Lesson 6.4	4A Chapter 6 Lesson 4	
Chapter 3 Item 11	Express improper fractions as mixed numbers, and mixed numbers as improper fractions.	4A pp. 177–184	Lesson 6.4	4A Chapter 6 Lesson 4	
	Use a bar model to represent a fraction of a set.	4A pp. 195–197	Lesson 6.7	4A Chapter 6 Lesson 8	Grade 3 students use pictures to find a fraction of a set in 3B Chapter 14 Lesson 5
Chapter 3 Items 16–17	Express a fraction as a decimal and a decimal as a fraction.	4B pp. 51–56	Lesson 7.5	4B Chapter 7 Lessons 1 and 2	
Chapter 4 Items 1, 5–7	Find equivalent fractions.	Support for this objective is included in Chapter 6.		4A Chapter 6 Lesson 2	3B Chapter 14 Lesson 2
Chapter 4 Item 2	Write an improper fraction for a model.	Support for this objective is included in Chapter 6.		4A Chapter 6 Lesson 4	
Chapter 4 Items 3, 11	Express a fraction as a decimal and a decimal as a fraction.	Support for this objective is included in Chapter 6.		4B Chapter 7 Lessons 1 and 2	
Chapter 4 Item 8	Subtract unlike fractions.	Support for this objective is included in Chapter 6.		4A Chapter 6 Lesson 2	
Chapter 4 Items 9–10	Express improper fractions as mixed numbers, and mixed numbers as improper fractions.	Support for this objective is included in Chapter 6.		4A Chapter 6 Lesson 4	
Chapter 4 Item 12	Find a fractional part of a number.	4A pp. 193–198	Lesson 6.7	4A Chapter 6 Lesson 8	
Chapter 4 Item 14, 16	Solve real–world problems involving fractions.	4A pp. 199–206	Lesson 6.8	4A Chapter 6 Lesson 8	
Chapter 4 Items 15, 17	Use a variety of strategies to solve word problems involving all four operations.	Support for this objective is included in Chapter 6.		4A Chapter 6 Lesson 8 (no division)	

For Additional Support: See the Grade 5 Chapters 3 and 4 Math in Focus Background Videos on Think Central <www.k6.thinkcentral.com>.

Fractions and Mixed Numbers

Students have learned...

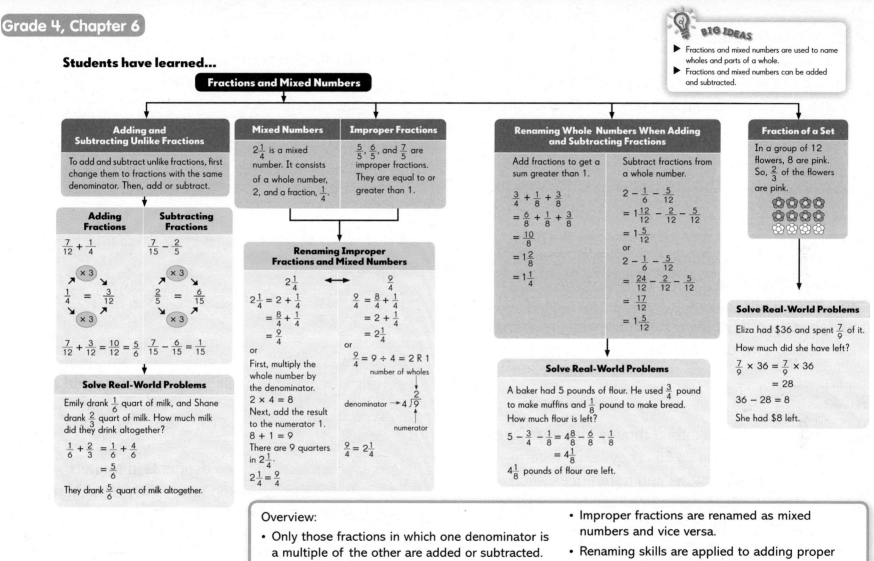

Fractions and Mixed Numbers

Adding and Subtracting Unlike Fractions

To add and subtract unlike fractions, first change them to fractions with the same denominator. Then, add or subtract.

Adding Fractions

$$\frac{7}{12} + \frac{1}{4}$$

$\frac{1}{4} = \frac{3}{12}$ (× 3)

$$\frac{7}{12} + \frac{3}{12} = \frac{10}{12} = \frac{5}{6}$$

Subtracting Fractions

$$\frac{7}{15} - \frac{2}{5}$$

$\frac{2}{5} = \frac{6}{15}$ (× 3)

$$\frac{7}{15} - \frac{6}{15} = \frac{1}{15}$$

Solve Real-World Problems

Emily drank $\frac{1}{6}$ quart of milk, and Shane drank $\frac{2}{3}$ quart of milk. How much milk did they drink altogether?

$$\frac{1}{6} + \frac{2}{3} = \frac{1}{6} + \frac{4}{6}$$
$$= \frac{5}{6}$$

They drank $\frac{5}{6}$ quart of milk altogether.

Mixed Numbers

$2\frac{1}{4}$ is a mixed number. It consists of a whole number, 2, and a fraction, $\frac{1}{4}$.

Improper Fractions

$\frac{5}{5}$, $\frac{6}{5}$, and $\frac{7}{5}$ are improper fractions. They are equal to or greater than 1.

Renaming Improper Fractions and Mixed Numbers

$$2\frac{1}{4} \longleftrightarrow \frac{9}{4}$$

$$2\frac{1}{4} = 2 + \frac{1}{4}$$
$$= \frac{8}{4} + \frac{1}{4}$$
$$= \frac{9}{4}$$

or

First, multiply the whole number by the denominator.
$2 \times 4 = 8$
Next, add the result to the numerator 1.
$8 + 1 = 9$
There are 9 quarters in $2\frac{1}{4}$.
$$2\frac{1}{4} = \frac{9}{4}$$

$$\frac{9}{4} = \frac{8}{4} + \frac{1}{4}$$
$$= 2 + \frac{1}{4}$$
$$= 2\frac{1}{4}$$

or

$$\frac{9}{4} = 9 \div 4 = 2 \text{ R } 1$$

number of wholes

denominator → $4\overline{)9}$ ← 2

numerator

$$\frac{9}{4} = 2\frac{1}{4}$$

Renaming Whole Numbers When Adding and Subtracting Fractions

Add fractions to get a sum greater than 1.

$$\frac{3}{4} + \frac{1}{8} + \frac{3}{8}$$
$$= \frac{6}{8} + \frac{1}{8} + \frac{3}{8}$$
$$= \frac{10}{8}$$
$$= 1\frac{2}{8}$$
$$= 1\frac{1}{4}$$

Subtract fractions from a whole number.

$$2 - \frac{1}{6} - \frac{5}{12}$$
$$= 1\frac{12}{12} - \frac{2}{12} - \frac{5}{12}$$
$$= 1\frac{5}{12}$$

or

$$2 - \frac{1}{6} - \frac{5}{12}$$
$$= \frac{24}{12} - \frac{2}{12} - \frac{5}{12}$$
$$= \frac{17}{12}$$
$$= 1\frac{5}{12}$$

Solve Real-World Problems

A baker had 5 pounds of flour. He used $\frac{3}{4}$ pound to make muffins and $\frac{1}{8}$ pound to make bread. How much flour is left?

$$5 - \frac{3}{4} - \frac{1}{8} = 4\frac{8}{8} - \frac{6}{8} - \frac{1}{8}$$
$$= 4\frac{1}{8}$$

$4\frac{1}{8}$ pounds of flour are left.

Fraction of a Set

In a group of 12 flowers, 8 are pink. So, $\frac{2}{3}$ of the flowers are pink.

Solve Real-World Problems

Eliza had $36 and spent $\frac{7}{9}$ of it. How much did she have left?

$$\frac{7}{9} \times 36 = \frac{7}{9} \times 36$$
$$= 28$$

$36 - 28 = 8$

She had $8 left.

Overview:

- Only those fractions in which one denominator is a multiple of the other are added or subtracted.
- Unlike fractions are compared.
- Fractions are multiplied by whole numbers.
- Improper fractions are renamed as mixed numbers and vice versa.
- Renaming skills are applied to adding proper fractions with sums greater than 1 and subtracting proper fractions from a whole number.

Decimal concepts are introduced with money—dollars and cents—in Grades 2 and 3, where students can work with them concretely using plastic coins and paper bills. It isn't until Grade 4 that decimals are generalized to their many other applications. At that time students are introduced to the concept of a decimal and how to add and subtract one- and two-place decimals.

Grade 2

Students see the decimal notation for dollars and cents for the first time. They learn how to write any money amount in either dollars or cents using words and the dollars and cents symbols. They add money amounts given in cents that total more than a dollar and write the answer in decimal form. Thus they combine the new skill of rewriting money amounts using decimals while reviewing the skill of adding two-digit numbers.

Grade 3

Students learn to add and subtract money amounts given in dollars and cents, such as $3.55. They learn several strategies for finding these sums and differences, such as using number bonds to separate the dollars and cents, and then combining the dollars with the dollars and the cents with the cents.

For example, to find the total cost of an item costing $5.35 and another item costing $2.40, students learn to use the decomposition strategy shown.

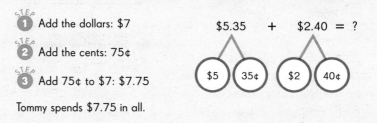

STEP 1 Add the dollars: $7

STEP 2 Add the cents: 75¢

STEP 3 Add 75¢ to $7: $7.75

Tommy spends $7.75 in all.

These strategies culminate in the standard place-value algorithm for adding and subtracting dollars and cents.

Grade 4

Students learn how to write decimals in tenths or hundredths as fractions, and how to write fractions as these decimals. They compare, add, and subtract these decimals first using models such as fraction circles, decimal squares, and number lines, and then using place-value concepts. They also learn how to round these decimals to the nearest whole number or the nearest tenth.

Chapter 10: Money

Transition Topic: Money and Decimals

Grade 3 Chapter 10 Pre-Test Items	Grade 3 Chapter 10 Pre-Test Item Objective	Additional Support for the Objective: Grade 2 Reteach	Additional Support for the Objective: Grade 2 Extra Practice	Grade 2 Teacher Edition Support	Going Back Further (Grade 1)
Items 1–4	Show and count money using coins and bills to $20.	2B pp. 29; 32–33; 35–40	Lesson 11.1	2B Chapter 11 Lesson 1	Grade 1 students count coins in 1B Chapter 19 Lessons 1–2
Items 5–6; 9–10	Write money amounts using $ and ¢.	2B pp. 36–38	Lesson 11.1	2B Chapter 11 Lesson 1	Grade 1 students write amounts up to $1 in 1B Chapter 19 Lessons 1–3
Items 7–8	Write dollars as cents and cents as dollars.	2B pp. 39–40	Lesson 11.1	2B Chapter 11 Lesson 1	Grade 1 students write amounts up to $1 in 1B Chapter 19 Lessons 1–3
	Compare amounts of money.	2B pp. 34; 41–44	Lesson 11.2	2B Chapter 11 Lesson 2	1B Chapter 19 Lesson 4
Items 11–12	Use bar models to solve real-world problems involving addition and subtraction of money.	2B pp. 45–48	Lesson 11.3	2B Chapter 11 Lesson 3	1B Chapter 19 Lesson 4 does not use bar models, but does have real-world problems

For Additional Support: See the Grade 3 Chapter 10 Math in Focus Background Videos on Think Central <www-k6.thinkcentral.com>.

Students have learned...

BIG IDEA Money amounts can be shown and counted using bills and coins.

identifying bills

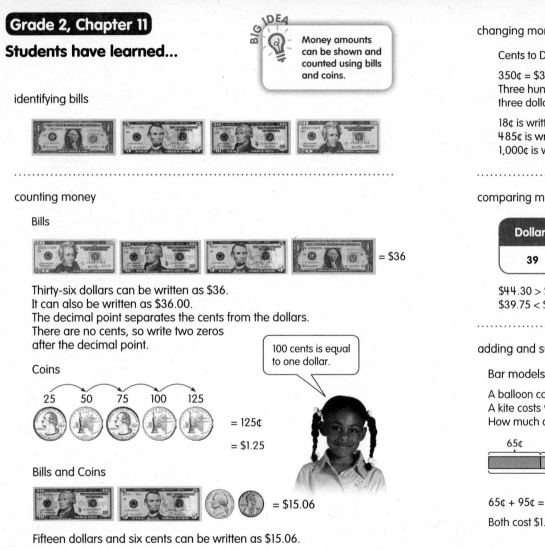

counting money

Bills

= $36

Thirty-six dollars can be written as $36.
It can also be written as $36.00.
The decimal point separates the cents from the dollars.
There are no cents, so write two zeros after the decimal point.

Coins

25 50 75 100 125

= 125¢
= $1.25

100 cents is equal to one dollar.

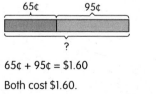
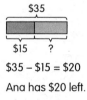

Bills and Coins

= $15.06

Fifteen dollars and six cents can be written as $15.06.

changing money

Cents to Dollars

350¢ = $3.50
Three hundred fifty cents is three dollars and fifty cents.

18¢ is written as $0.18.
485¢ is written as $4.85.
1,000¢ is written as $10.00.

Dollars to Cents

$2.55 = 255¢
Two dollars and fifty-five cents is two hundred fifty-five cents.

$8.65 is written as 865¢.
$0.07 is written as 7¢.
$0.90 is written as 90¢.

comparing money

Dollars	Cents
39	75

Dollars	Cents
44	30

$44.30 > $39.75
$39.75 < $44.30

adding and subtracting money

Bar models can be used to solve word-problems.

A balloon costs 65¢.
A kite costs 95¢.
How much do both cost?

65¢   95¢

?

65¢ + 95¢ = $1.60

Both cost $1.60.

Ana has $35.
She spends $15.
How much money does she have left?

$35

$15   ?

$35 − $15 = $20

Ana has $20 left.

Overview:

• Emphasis is on the dollar and cents notation with the decimal point.

• Building on what they have learned about comparing whole numbers, children learn to compare money amounts.

• Real-world problems include changing money from cents notation to dollar and cents notation.

Chapter 7: Decimals and Chapter 8: Adding and Subtracting Decimals

Transition Topic: Money and Decimals

Grade 4 Chapters 7–8 Pre-Test Items	Grade 4 Chapters 7–8 Pre-Test Item Objective	Additional Support for the Objective: Grade 3 Reteach	Additional Support for the Objective: Grade 3 Extra Practice	Grade 3 Teacher Edition Support	Going Back Further (Grade 2)
	Use rounding to estimate sums and differences.	3A pp. 31–34	Lesson 2.4	3A Chapter 2 Lesson 4	2B Chapter 10 Lesson 5
Chapter 7 Items 2; 3	Identify numerator and denominator.	3B p. 84	Lesson 14.1	3B Chapter 14 Lesson 1	Grade 2 students study parts of a fraction but not their formal names in 2B Chapter 12 Lesson 1
Chapter 7 Item 1	Use models to identify equivalent fractions.	3B pp. 85–87	Lesson 14.2	3B Chapter 14 Lesson 3	
	Use a number line to identify equivalent fractions.	3B p. 88	Lesson 14.2	3B Chapter 14 Lesson 2	
Chapter 7 Items 11–14	Use multiplication and division to find equivalent fractions.	3B pp. 89–96	Lesson 14.3	3B Chapter 14 Lesson 3	
Chapter 7 Items 15–16	Compare and order fractions.	3B pp. 97–106	Lesson 14.4	3B Chapter 14 Lesson 4	2B Chapter 12 Lesson 2
Chapter 8 Items 2–9	Read and write numbers to 1,000 in standard form, expanded form, and word form.	3A pp. 1–2; 5–9 See also Gr. 2B pp. 35–37; 41–44	Lessons 1.1 and 1.2 See also Gr. 2 Lessons 11.1 and 11.2.	3A Chapter 1 Lesson 1	2A Chapter 1 Lesson 2
Chapter 8 Item 1	Subtract from three-digit numbers with regrouping in hundreds, tens, and ones.	3A pp. 59–64	Lesson 4.3	3A Chapter 4 Lesson 3	2A Chapter 3 Lesson 3
	Add money in different ways without regrouping.	3B pp. 1–3	Lesson 10.1	3B Chapter 10 Lesson 1	2B Chapter 11 Lesson 1 (informal)
	Add money in different ways with regrouping.	3B pp. 9–11; 15–16	Lesson 10.1	3B Chapter 10 Lesson 1	2B Chapter 11 Lesson 1 (informal)
	Subtract money in different ways without regrouping.	3B pp. 17–21	Lesson 10.2	3B Chapter 10 Lesson 2	
	Subtract money in different ways with regrouping.	3B pp. 25–28; 29–30	Lesson 10.2	3B Chapter 10 Lesson 2	

For Additional Support: See the Grade 4 Chapters 7 and 8 Math in Focus Background Videos on Think Central <www-k6.thinkcentral.com>.

Students have learned...

Money

BIG IDEA
▶ You can add and subtract money the same way you add and subtract whole numbers.

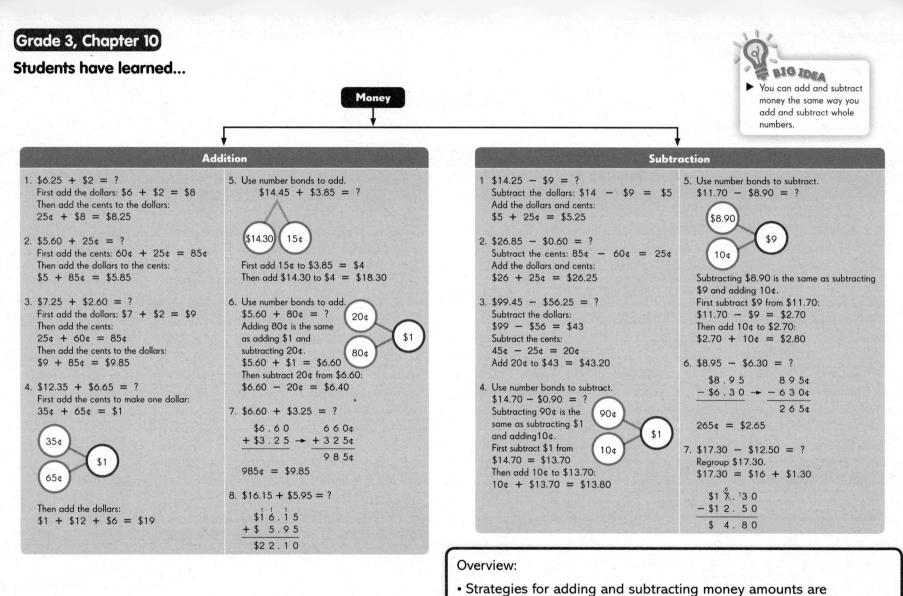

Addition

1. $6.25 + $2 = ?
   First add the dollars: $6 + $2 = $8
   Then add the cents to the dollars:
   25¢ + $8 = $8.25

2. $5.60 + 25¢ = ?
   First add the cents: 60¢ + 25¢ = 85¢
   Then add the dollars to the cents:
   $5 + 85¢ = $5.85

3. $7.25 + $2.60 = ?
   First add the dollars: $7 + $2 = $9
   Then add the cents:
   25¢ + 60¢ = 85¢
   Then add the cents to the dollars:
   $9 + 85¢ = $9.85

4. $12.35 + $6.65 = ?
   First add the cents to make one dollar:
   35¢ + 65¢ = $1

   35¢ ──┐
         $1
   65¢ ──┘

   Then add the dollars:
   $1 + $12 + $6 = $19

5. Use number bonds to add.
   $14.45 + $3.85 = ?

   $14.30   15¢

   First add 15¢ to $3.85 = $4
   Then add $14.30 to $4 = $18.30

6. Use number bonds to add.
   $5.60 + 80¢ = ?
   Adding 80¢ is the same
   as adding $1 and
   subtracting 20¢.
   $5.60 + $1 = $6.60
   Then subtract 20¢ from $6.60:
   $6.60 − 20¢ = $6.40

   20¢ ──┐
         $1
   80¢ ──┘

7. $6.60 + $3.25 = ?

   $6 . 6 0   6 6 0¢
   + $3 . 2 5 → + 3 2 5¢
   ─────────   ─────────
                   9 8 5¢

   985¢ = $9.85

8. $16.15 + $5.95 = ?

   ¹ ¹ ¹
   $1 6 . 1 5
   + $ 5 . 9 5
   ─────────────
   $2 2 . 1 0

Subtraction

1. $14.25 − $9 = ?
   Subtract the dollars: $14 − $9 = $5
   Add the dollars and cents:
   $5 + 25¢ = $5.25

2. $26.85 − $0.60 = ?
   Subtract the cents: 85¢ − 60¢ = 25¢
   Add the dollars and cents:
   $26 + 25¢ = $26.25

3. $99.45 − $56.25 = ?
   Subtract the dollars:
   $99 − $56 = $43
   Subtract the cents:
   45¢ − 25¢ = 20¢
   Add 20¢ to $43 = $43.20

4. Use number bonds to subtract.
   $14.70 − $0.90 = ?
   Subtracting 90¢ is the
   same as subtracting $1
   and adding 10¢.
   First subtract $1 from
   $14.70 = $13.70
   Then add 10¢ to $13.70:
   10¢ + $13.70 = $13.80

   90¢ ──┐
         $1
   10¢ ──┘

5. Use number bonds to subtract.
   $11.70 − $8.90 = ?

   $8.90 ──┐
           $9
   10¢ ────┘

   Subtracting $8.90 is the same as subtracting
   $9 and adding 10¢.
   First subtract $9 from $11.70:
   $11.70 − $9 = $2.70
   Then add 10¢ to $2.70:
   $2.70 + 10¢ = $2.80

6. $8.95 − $6.30 = ?

   $8 . 9 5   8 9 5¢
   − $6 . 3 0 → − 6 3 0¢
   ─────────   ─────────
                   2 6 5¢

   265¢ = $2.65

7. $17.30 − $12.50 = ?
   Regroup $17.30.
   $17.30 = $16 + $1.30

           6
   $1 7̸ . ¹3 0
   − $1 2 . 5 0
   ─────────────
   $ 4 . 8 0

Overview:

- Strategies for adding and subtracting money amounts are emphasized, with attention to mental math strategies.

- The strategies culminate in the standard place-value algorithms for adding and subtracting.

Grade 5: Chapters 8, 9, and 10

Chapter 8: Decimals; Chapter 9: Multiplying and Dividing Decimals; and Chapter 10: Percent

Transition Topic: Money and Decimals

Grade 5 Chapters 8–10 Pre-Test Items	Grade 5 Chapters 8–10 Pre-Test Item Objective	Additional Support for the Objective: Grade 4 Reteach	Additional Support for the Objective: Grade 4 Extra Practice	Grade 4 Teacher Edition Support	Going Back Further (Grade 3)
	Represent and interpret hundredths models.	4B pp. 11–12, 16–17	Lesson 7.2	4B Chapter 8 Lesson 1	3B Chapter 11 Lesson 1 (informal: metric measurement)
Chapter 8 Items 5, 8–9	Compare and order decimals.	4B pp. 29–32, 39–46	Lesson 7.3	4B Chapter 8 Lesson 2	3B Chapter 11 Lesson 4
Chapter 8 Items 3–4, 12–17	Round decimals to the nearest whole number or tenth.	4B pp. 47–50	Lesson 7.4	4B Chapter 8 Lesson 2	
Chapter 8 Items 10-11, 18	Express a fraction as a decimal and a decimal as a fraction.	Support for this objective is included in Chapter 3.		4B Chapter 8 Lesson 3	
Chapter 8 Items 1, 7–12, 21	Read and write hundredths in decimal and fractional forms.	4B pp. 11–15, 18–28	Lesson 7.2	4B Chapter 8 Lesson 3	
Chapter 8 Item 1	Use different methods to multiply whole numbers up to four-digits by one-digit and two-digit numbers with or without regrouping.	Support for this objective is included in Chapter 2.		4A Chapter 2 Lessons 2 and 3 (up to three-digit by two-digit)	3A Chapter 7 Lessons 1–3
Chapter 9 Items 3, 16–17	Estimate products and quotients.	Support for this objective is included in Chapter 2.		4A Chapter 2 Lessons 2 and 4	
Chapter 9 Items 4–9	Multiply by ones, tens, and hundreds mentally.	3A pp. 123–128	Lesson 7.1	4A Chapter 2 Lessons 2 and 3	3A Chapter 7 Lesson 1
Chapter 9 Items 10–15	Use patterns to divide multiples of 10 and 100.	3A pp. 142–144	Lesson 8.1	4A Chapter 2 Lessons 2 and 4	3A Chapter 8 Lesson 1
Chapter 9 Items 18–19	Use a variety of strategies to solve word problems involving all four operations.	Support for this objective is included in Chapter 2.		4B Chapter 8 Lesson 3	3A Chapter 9 Lesson 4
Chapter 10 Item 2	Divide up to a four-digit number by a one-digit number with regrouping, and with or without remainders.	Support for this objective is included in Chapter 2.		4A Chapter 3 Lesson 4	3A Chapter 8 Lesson 5

For Additional Support: See the Grade 5 Chapters 8, 9, and 10 Math in Focus Background Videos on Think Central <www.k6.thinkcentral.com>.

Students have learned...

BIG IDEAS

▶ Decimals are another way to show amounts that are parts of a whole.
▶ A decimal has a decimal point to the right of the ones place and digits to the right of the decimal point.

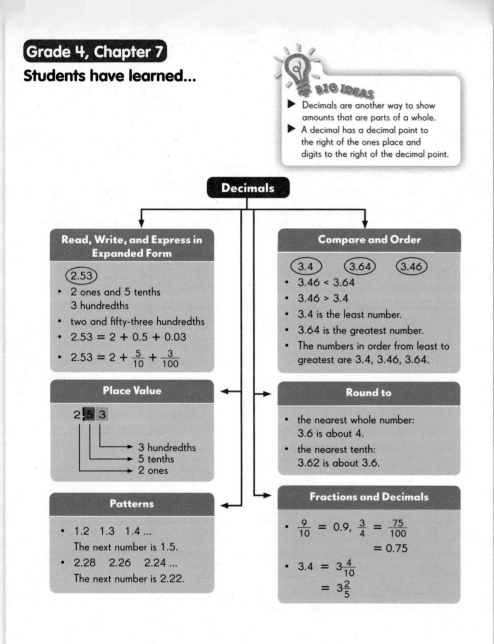

Decimals

Read, Write, and Express in Expanded Form

(2.53)

• 2 ones and 5 tenths
  3 hundredths
• two and fifty-three hundredths
• 2.53 = 2 + 0.5 + 0.03
• 2.53 = 2 + $\frac{5}{10}$ + $\frac{3}{100}$

Place Value

2.53

→ 3 hundredths
→ 5 tenths
→ 2 ones

Patterns

• 1.2 1.3 1.4 ...
  The next number is 1.5.
• 2.28 2.26 2.24 ...
  The next number is 2.22.

Compare and Order

(3.4)   (3.64)   (3.46)

• 3.46 < 3.64
• 3.46 > 3.4
• 3.4 is the least number.
• 3.64 is the greatest number.
• The numbers in order from least to greatest are 3.4, 3.46, 3.64.

Round to

• the nearest whole number:
  3.6 is about 4.
• the nearest tenth:
  3.62 is about 3.6.

Fractions and Decimals

• $\frac{9}{10}$ = 0.9, $\frac{3}{4}$ = $\frac{75}{100}$
                        = 0.75
• 3.4 = $3\frac{4}{10}$
      = $3\frac{2}{5}$

Overview:

• In the earlier grades, students were introduced to two-place decimals in the context of money.

• Now students learn to model, read, write, compare, and round decimal numbers to hundredths using models such as fraction circles, decimal squares, and number lines.

• Decimals are written in all three forms: standard form, word form, and expanded form.

• Students connect decimals to fractions by writing equivalent fractions and decimals.

• Students learn to complete a sequence of decimals by studying the number pattern.

Students have learned...

BIG IDEA

▶ Decimals can be added and subtracted in the same ways as whole numbers.

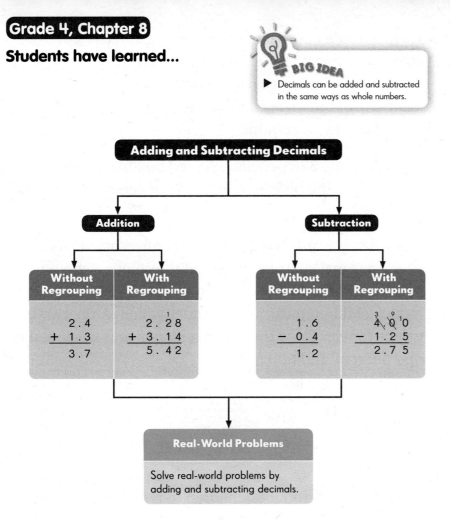

Adding and Subtracting Decimals

Addition

Without Regrouping	With Regrouping
2.4 + 1.3 ——— 3.7	2.28 + 3.14 ——— 5.42

Subtraction

Without Regrouping	With Regrouping
1.6 − 0.4 ——— 1.2	4.00 − 1.25 ——— 2.75

Real-World Problems

Solve real-world problems by adding and subtracting decimals.

Overview:

- In Grades 2 and 3, students learned how to use bar models to solve real-world problems for whole numbers.

- In Grade 4, this skill is extended to drawing bar models to solve problems using decimals.

- Decimal addition and subtraction is developed using decimal squares and place-value chips.

- The algorithms develop through recording the steps of the place-value models.

- Decimals are rounded to the nearest tenth or whole number, so that estimates can be made later in the year.

Problem solving involving the four operations uses the signature Singapore approach: bar modeling. Bar models help students to visualize complex relationships. With these visual representations, even difficult fraction relationships become approachable. Another advantage of using this approach is the ease with which it transfers to algebraic problems as labeling the bar models clarifies the relationships among numbers and variables in all positions in the associated equations.

Grade 2

Students model addition and subtraction real-world problems using connecting cubes in Grade 1. In Grade 2, the numbers become greater and connecting cubes become cumbersome, motivating the transition to bar models, as shown below.

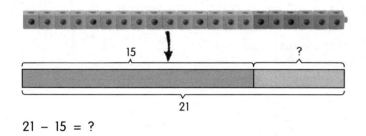

$$21 - 15 = ?$$

Later in the year, students use bar models for multiplication and division. The division models include both finding the number of equal groups and finding how many items are in one of the equal groups.

With bar models children move away from a "key word" strategy and concentrate more on the relationship being described. Consider a problem such as:

A red box has 326 pencils. The red box has 78 fewer pencils than the blue box. How many pencils are in the blue box?

Using a key word strategy, children often use the word *fewer* to signal subtraction, when the solution should involve addition. When solving this problem using a bar model, children must first consider which of the two bars will be longer. Once the bars are drawn and labeled, the operation of addition is clear.

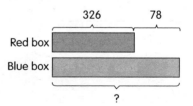

Grade 2 also introduces children to two-step real-world problems. At this grade level, two-step problems are presented as two separate questions, so that children know they must find two answers. In later grades, these intermediate questions are suppressed and children reason logically to deduce these intermediate questions and answers.

Grade 3

Students expand their bar model skills to one- and two-step problems that involve larger numbers and more complex relationships, including the comparison relationship that can be indicated by multiplication. They begin to substitute letters for missing numbers in bar models and related number sentences as they solve one- and two-step problems.

When modeling multiplication and division, they learn to solve problems using the *unitary method*. In its simplest form, the idea is this:

- If you know how many items are in one unit, to find how many are in x units, you multiply by x.

- If you know how many items are in x units, you can divide by x to find how many items are in 1 unit.

In Grades 4 and 5, these ideas are used to develop fraction concepts.

After students learn to convert measurements from one metric unit to another, students solve measurement problems using bar models.

Grade 4

Bar models help students visualize two-step problems and comparisons that involve fractions and decimals. The bar modeling skills are similar to those for whole-number addition and subtraction, but the computations involve fractions and decimals. These skills are the foundation needed to model problems in Grade 5 that involve multiplication and division of fractions, decimals, and percents.

Worth noting is the thoroughness with which these real-world problems prepare students for algebra. Using letters for missing numbers in bar models and their related number sentences will assure that students are comfortable with the idea of the algebraic unknown.

Instructional Pathway for Transition

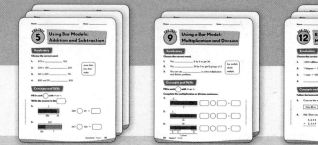

Grade 3: Chapters 5, 9, and 12

Chapter 5: Using Bar Models: Addition and Subtraction;
Chapter 9: Using Bar Models: Multiplication and Division; and Chapter 12: Real-World Problems: Measurement

Transition Topic: Problem Solving and Bar Models

Grade 3 Chapters 5, 9, and 12 Pre-Test Items	Grade 3 Chapters 5, 9, and 12 Pre-Test Item Objective	Additional Support for the Objective: Grade 2 Reteach	Additional Support for the Objective: Grade 2 Extra Practice	Grade 2 Teacher Edition Support	Going Back Further (Grade 1)
Chapter 5 Items 5–10	Use bar models to solve addition and subtraction problems.	2A pp. 83–100	Lessons 4.1–4.3	2A Chapter 8 Lesson 5	1A Chapter 3 Lesson 1
Chapter 5 Items 4; 5	Model addition as joining sets.	2A pp. 84–85; 88; 89–90	Lessons 4.1 and 4.2	2A Chapter 4 Lesson 1	1A Chapter 9 Lesson 1
Chapter 5 Items 6; 8	Model subtraction as taking away.	2A pp. 86–87; 91–92	Lessons 4.1 and 4.2	2A Chapter 4 Lesson 2	1A Chapter 9 Lesson 1
Chapter 5 Items 7–10	Model addition and subtraction as comparing sets.	2A pp. 93–96	Lesson 4.3	2A Chapter 4 Lesson 3	
	Use bar models to solve two-step addition and subtraction problems.	2A pp. 97–100	Lesson 4.4	2A Chapter 4 Lesson 4	
Chapter 9 Items 3; 7	Use bar models to solve real-world multiplication problems.	2B pp. 113–114	Lesson 16.1	2B Chapter 16 Lesson 3	
Chapter 9 Item 4	Write multiplication sentences to solve real-word problems.	2B pp. 113–114	Lesson 16.1	2B Chapter 16 Lesson 3	
Chapter 9 Items 3; 8	Use bar models to solve division word problems.	2B pp. 115–118	Lesson 16.2	2B Chapter 16 Lesson 3	
Chapter 9 Items 5–6	Write division sentences to solve word problems.	2B pp. 115–118	Lesson 16.2	2B Chapter 16 Lesson 3	
Chapter 12 Items 4; 10	Model addition and subtraction as comparing sets.	2A pp. 93–97	Lesson 4.3	2A Chapter 4 Lesson 3	
Chapter 12 Items 4; 10	Use bar models to solve problems about mass.	2A pp. 173–176	Lesson 8.5	2A Chapter 8 Lesson 5	
Chapter 12 Items 4; 10	Use bar models, addition, and subtraction to solve real-world problems about volume.	2A pp. 185–188	Lesson 9.3	2A Chapter 9 Lesson 3	
Chapter 12 Items 4; 11–12	Use bar models to solve real-world problems on measurement and money.	2B pp. 119–126	Lesson 16.3	2A Chapter 4 Lesson 3 (money); Chapter 7 Lesson 5 (measurement)	

For Additional Support: See the Grade 3 Chapters 5, 9, and 12 Math in Focus Background Videos on Think Central <www-k6.thinkcentral.com>.

Problem Solving and Bar Models

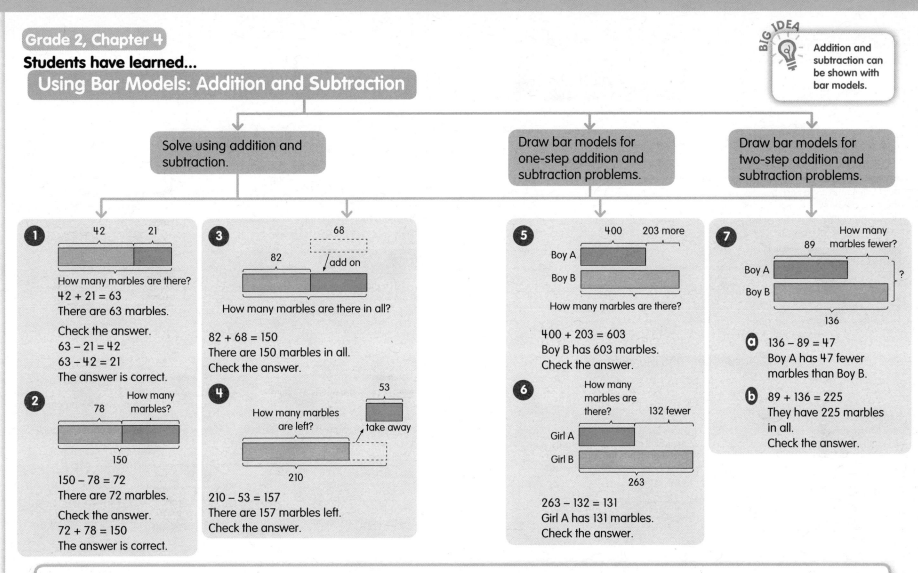

Grade 2, Chapter 4

Students have learned...

Using Bar Models: Addition and Subtraction

BIG IDEA
Addition and subtraction can be shown with bar models.

Solve using addition and subtraction.

Draw bar models for one-step addition and subtraction problems.

Draw bar models for two-step addition and subtraction problems.

1
42   21

How many marbles are there?
42 + 21 = 63
There are 63 marbles.

Check the answer.
63 − 21 = 42
63 − 42 = 21
The answer is correct.

2
How many marbles?
78

150

150 − 78 = 72
There are 72 marbles.

Check the answer.
72 + 78 = 150
The answer is correct.

3
68
82   add on

How many marbles are there in all?

82 + 68 = 150
There are 150 marbles in all.
Check the answer.

4
53
How many marbles are left?   take away

210

210 − 53 = 157
There are 157 marbles left.
Check the answer.

5
400   203 more
Boy A
Boy B

How many marbles are there?

400 + 203 = 603
Boy B has 603 marbles.
Check the answer.

6
How many marbles are there?   132 fewer
Girl A
Girl B
263

263 − 132 = 131
Girl A has 131 marbles.
Check the answer.

7
How many marbles fewer?
89
Boy A   ?
Boy B
136

a 136 − 89 = 47
Boy A has 47 fewer marbles than Boy B.

b 89 + 136 = 225
They have 225 marbles in all.
Check the answer.

Overview:
- Part-part-whole models are used for some addition or subtraction problems, as in Examples 1–4.

- Adding on or taking away can be shown using a second bar, as in Examples 3 and 4.
- Comparison problems, as in Examples 5 an 6, and two-step problems, as in Example 7, use two bars, one for each piece of data.

Problem Solving and Bar Models

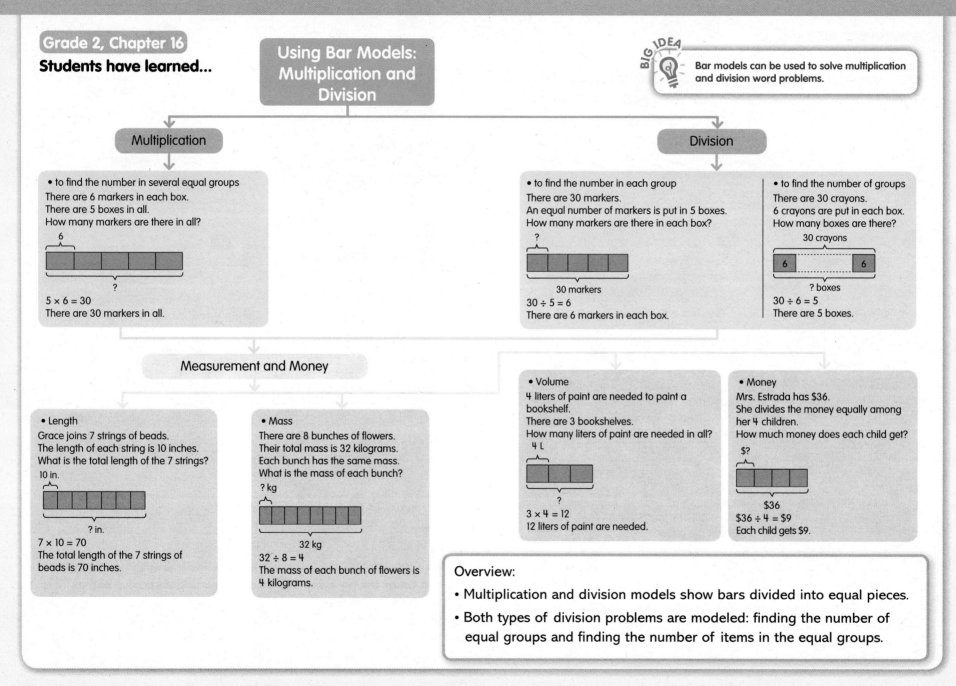

Grade 2, Chapter 16

Students have learned...

Using Bar Models: Multiplication and Division

BIG IDEA Bar models can be used to solve multiplication and division word problems.

Multiplication

• to find the number in several equal groups

There are 6 markers in each box.
There are 5 boxes in all.
How many markers are there in all?

6

?

$5 \times 6 = 30$
There are 30 markers in all.

Division

• to find the number in each group

There are 30 markers.
An equal number of markers is put in 5 boxes.
How many markers are there in each box?

?

30 markers
$30 \div 5 = 6$
There are 6 markers in each box.

• to find the number of groups

There are 30 crayons.
6 crayons are put in each box.
How many boxes are there?

30 crayons

6   6

? boxes
$30 \div 6 = 5$
There are 5 boxes.

Measurement and Money

• Length

Grace joins 7 strings of beads.
The length of each string is 10 inches.
What is the total length of the 7 strings?

10 in.

? in.
$7 \times 10 = 70$
The total length of the 7 strings of beads is 70 inches.

• Mass

There are 8 bunches of flowers.
Their total mass is 32 kilograms.
Each bunch has the same mass.
What is the mass of each bunch?

? kg

32 kg
$32 \div 8 = 4$
The mass of each bunch of flowers is 4 kilograms.

• Volume

4 liters of paint are needed to paint a bookshelf.
There are 3 bookshelves.
How many liters of paint are needed in all?

4 L

?
$3 \times 4 = 12$
12 liters of paint are needed.

• Money

Mrs. Estrada has $36.
She divides the money equally among her 4 children.
How much money does each child get?

$?

$36
$36 \div 4 = $9
Each child gets $9.

Overview:

• Multiplication and division models show bars divided into equal pieces.

• Both types of division problems are modeled: finding the number of equal groups and finding the number of items in the equal groups.

Grade 4: Chapter 6

Chapter 6: Fractions and Mixed Numbers

Transition Topic: Problem Solving and Bar Models

Grade 4 Chapter 6 Pre-Test Items	Grade 4 Chapter 6 Pre-Test Item Objective	Additional Support for the Objective: Grade 3 Reteach	Additional Support for the Objective: Grade 3 Extra Practice	Grade 3 Teacher Edition Support	Going Back Further (Grade 2)
Item 3	Use models to identify equivalent fractions.	3B pp. 85–86	Lesson 14.2	3B Chapter 14 Lesson 1	2B Chapter 12 Lesson 1
Item 10	Add two or three like fractions with sums of 1.	3B pp. 107–110		3B Chapter 14 Lesson 5	2B Chapter 12 Lesson 3
Item 11	Use models to identify equivalent fractions.	3B pp. 110–111		3B Chapter 14 Lesson 5	2B Chapter 12 Lesson 3
Item 9	Find the number of items in a fraction of a set.	3B pp. 115–116	Lesson 14.5	3B Chapter 14 Lesson 6	

For Additional Support: See the Grade 4 Chapter 6 Math in Focus Background Videos on Think Central <www-k6.thinkcentral.com>.

Problem Solving and Bar Models

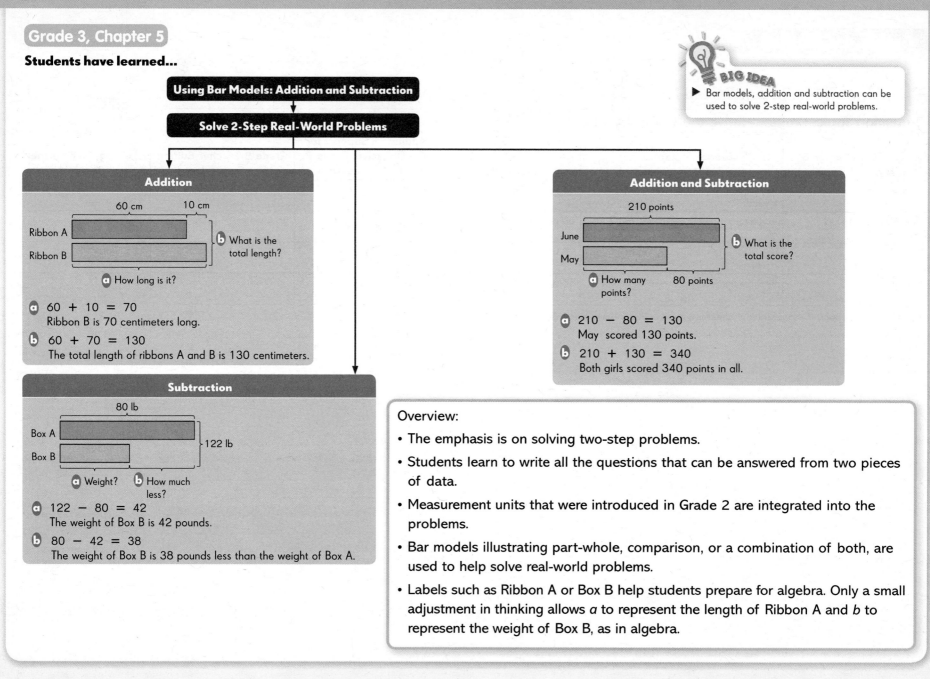

Students have learned...

Using Bar Models: Addition and Subtraction

Solve 2-Step Real-World Problems

BIG IDEA

▶ Bar models, addition and subtraction can be used to solve 2-step real-world problems.

Addition

60 cm   10 cm

Ribbon A

Ribbon B

b What is the total length?

a How long is it?

a 60 + 10 = 70
Ribbon B is 70 centimeters long.

b 60 + 70 = 130
The total length of ribbons A and B is 130 centimeters.

Subtraction

80 lb

Box A

Box B

122 lb

a Weight?   **b** How much less?

a 122 − 80 = 42
The weight of Box B is 42 pounds.

b 80 − 42 = 38
The weight of Box B is 38 pounds less than the weight of Box A.

Addition and Subtraction

210 points

June

May

b What is the total score?

a How many points?   80 points

a 210 − 80 = 130
May scored 130 points.

b 210 + 130 = 340
Both girls scored 340 points in all.

Overview:

- The emphasis is on solving two-step problems.
- Students learn to write all the questions that can be answered from two pieces of data.
- Measurement units that were introduced in Grade 2 are integrated into the problems.
- Bar models illustrating part-whole, comparison, or a combination of both, are used to help solve real-world problems.
- Labels such as Ribbon A or Box B help students prepare for algebra. Only a small adjustment in thinking allows *a* to represent the length of Ribbon A and *b* to represent the weight of Box B, as in algebra.

Problem Solving and Bar Models

Students have learned...

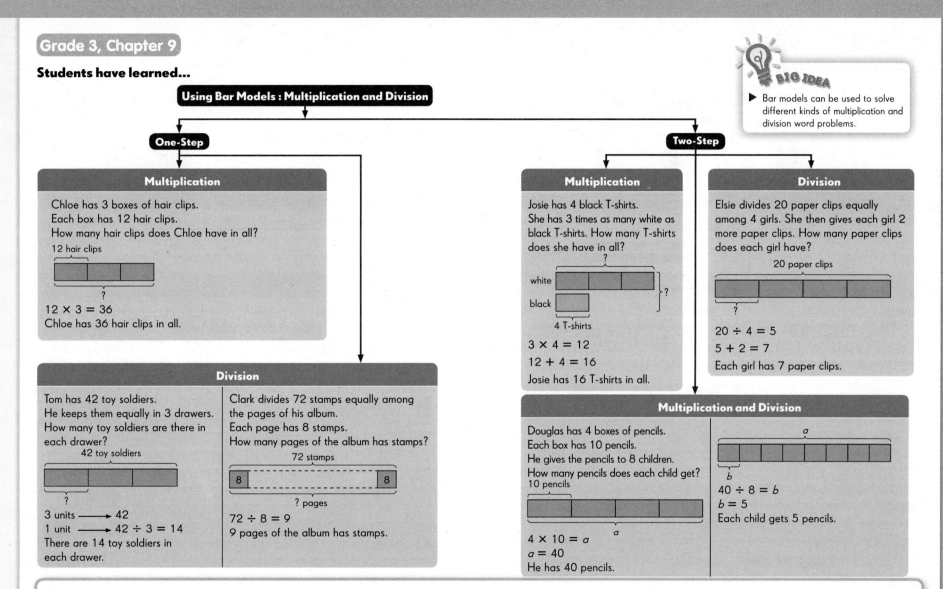

BIG IDEA

► Bar models can be used to solve different kinds of multiplication and division word problems.

Using Bar Models : Multiplication and Division

One-Step

Multiplication

Chloe has 3 boxes of hair clips.
Each box has 12 hair clips.
How many hair clips does Chloe have in all?

12 hair clips

?

$12 \times 3 = 36$
Chloe has 36 hair clips in all.

Division

Tom has 42 toy soldiers.
He keeps them equally in 3 drawers.
How many toy soldiers are there in each drawer?

42 toy soldiers

?

3 units ⟶ 42
1 unit ⟶ $42 \div 3 = 14$
There are 14 toy soldiers in each drawer.

Clark divides 72 stamps equally among the pages of his album.
Each page has 8 stamps.
How many pages of the album has stamps?

72 stamps

8   8

? pages

$72 \div 8 = 9$
9 pages of the album has stamps.

Two-Step

Multiplication

Josie has 4 black T-shirts.
She has 3 times as many white as black T-shirts. How many T-shirts does she have in all?

?

white

black

?

4 T-shirts

$3 \times 4 = 12$
$12 + 4 = 16$
Josie has 16 T-shirts in all.

Division

Elsie divides 20 paper clips equally among 4 girls. She then gives each girl 2 more paper clips. How many paper clips does each girl have?

20 paper clips

?

$20 \div 4 = 5$
$5 + 2 = 7$
Each girl has 7 paper clips.

Multiplication and Division

Douglas has 4 boxes of pencils.
Each box has 10 pencils.
He gives the pencils to 8 children.
How many pencils does each child get?

10 pencils

$4 \times 10 = a$
$a = 40$
He has 40 pencils.

a

b

a

$40 \div 8 = b$
$b = 5$
Each child gets 5 pencils.

Overview:

• The division strategy called the *unitary method*, which uses bar models, is developed and used to find the number of items in a given number of equal groups. Letters are introduced to represent the unknown number on a bar model and in its related number sentence.

• Two-step problems are emphasized, with students selecting from all four operations.

Problem Solving and Bar Models

Students have learned...

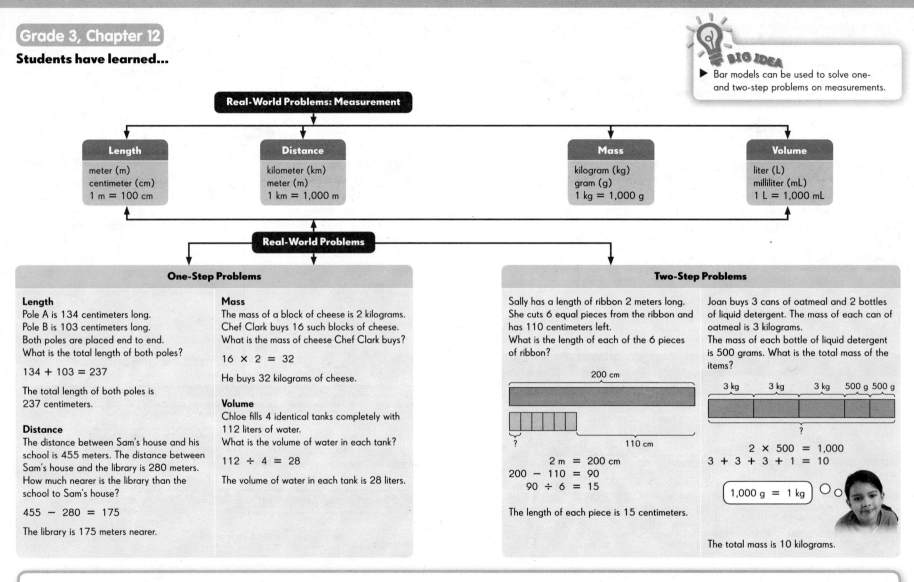

BIG IDEA
▶ Bar models can be used to solve one- and two-step problems on measurements.

Real-World Problems: Measurement

Length	Distance	Mass	Volume
meter (m)	kilometer (km)	kilogram (kg)	liter (L)
centimeter (cm)	meter (m)	gram (g)	milliliter (mL)
1 m = 100 cm	1 km = 1,000 m	1 kg = 1,000 g	1 L = 1,000 mL

Real-World Problems

One-Step Problems

Length
Pole A is 134 centimeters long.
Pole B is 103 centimeters long.
Both poles are placed end to end.
What is the total length of both poles?

134 + 103 = 237

The total length of both poles is 237 centimeters.

Distance
The distance between Sam's house and his school is 455 meters. The distance between Sam's house and the library is 280 meters. How much nearer is the library than the school to Sam's house?

455 − 280 = 175

The library is 175 meters nearer.

Mass
The mass of a block of cheese is 2 kilograms. Chef Clark buys 16 such blocks of cheese. What is the mass of cheese Chef Clark buys?

16 × 2 = 32

He buys 32 kilograms of cheese.

Volume
Chloe fills 4 identical tanks completely with 112 liters of water.
What is the volume of water in each tank?

112 ÷ 4 = 28

The volume of water in each tank is 28 liters.

Two-Step Problems

Sally has a length of ribbon 2 meters long. She cuts 6 equal pieces from the ribbon and has 110 centimeters left.
What is the length of each of the 6 pieces of ribbon?

200 cm

?   110 cm

2 m = 200 cm
200 − 110 = 90
90 ÷ 6 = 15

The length of each piece is 15 centimeters.

Joan buys 3 cans of oatmeal and 2 bottles of liquid detergent. The mass of each can of oatmeal is 3 kilograms.
The mass of each bottle of liquid detergent is 500 grams. What is the total mass of the items?

3 kg	3 kg	3 kg	500 g	500 g

?

2 × 500 = 1,000
3 + 3 + 3 + 1 = 10

1,000 g = 1 kg

The total mass is 10 kilograms.

Overview:

• Bar models and part-whole strategies are applied to measurement problems.

• Students are weaned away from modeling one-step problems but encouraged to use them for more complex relationships.

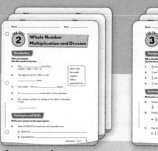
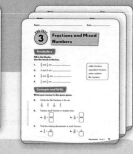

Grade 5: Chapters 2 and 3

Chapter 2: Whole Number Multiplication and Division and Chapter 3: Fractions and Mixed Numbers

Transition Topic: Problem Solving and Models

Grade 5 Chapters 2–3 Pre-Test Items	Grade 5 Chapters 2–3 Pre-Test Item Objective	Additional Support for the Objective: Grade 4 Reteach	Additional Support for the Objective: Grade 4 Extra Practice	Grade 4 Teacher Edition Support	Going Back Further (Grade 3)
Chapter 2 Items 4, 20–22	Use a variety of strategies to solve word problems involving all four operations.	4A pp. 81–88	Lesson 3.5	4A Chapter 3 Lesson 5	3A Chapter 8 Lesson 2
Chapter 2 Items 7–8	Use bar models to represent information and solve problems.	4A pp. 82–86	Lesson 5.1	4A Chapter 3 Lesson 5	3B Chapter 14 Lesson 5
Chapter 3 Items 18–19	Solve real-world problems involving fractions.	4A pp. 199–206	Lesson 6.8	4A Chapter 6 Lesson 8	3B Chapter 14 Lesson 5

For Additional Support: See the Grade 5 Chapters 2 and 3 Math in Focus Background Videos on Think Central <www.k6.thinkcentral.com>.

Problem Solving and Bar Models

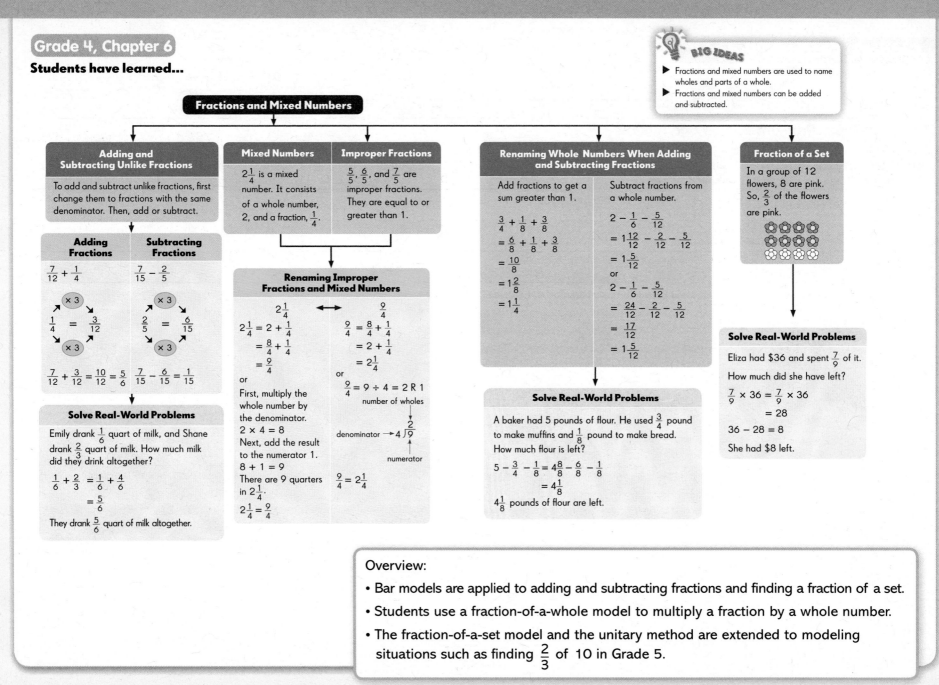

Students have learned...

BIG IDEAS
- ▶ Fractions and mixed numbers are used to name wholes and parts of a whole.
- ▶ Fractions and mixed numbers can be added and subtracted.

Fractions and Mixed Numbers

Adding and Subtracting Unlike Fractions

To add and subtract unlike fractions, first change them to fractions with the same denominator. Then, add or subtract.

Adding Fractions	Subtracting Fractions
$\frac{7}{12} + \frac{1}{4}$	$\frac{7}{15} - \frac{2}{5}$
$\frac{1}{4} = \frac{3}{12}$ (×3)	$\frac{2}{5} = \frac{6}{15}$ (×3)
$\frac{7}{12} + \frac{3}{12} = \frac{10}{12} = \frac{5}{6}$	$\frac{7}{15} - \frac{6}{15} = \frac{1}{15}$

Solve Real-World Problems

Emily drank $\frac{1}{6}$ quart of milk, and Shane drank $\frac{2}{3}$ quart of milk. How much milk did they drink altogether?

$$\frac{1}{6} + \frac{2}{3} = \frac{1}{6} + \frac{4}{6}$$
$$= \frac{5}{6}$$

They drank $\frac{5}{6}$ quart of milk altogether.

Mixed Numbers

$2\frac{1}{4}$ is a mixed number. It consists of a whole number, 2, and a fraction, $\frac{1}{4}$.

Improper Fractions

$\frac{5}{5}$, $\frac{6}{5}$, and $\frac{7}{5}$ are improper fractions. They are equal to or greater than 1.

Renaming Improper Fractions and Mixed Numbers

$$2\frac{1}{4} \longleftrightarrow \frac{9}{4}$$

$$2\frac{1}{4} = 2 + \frac{1}{4} \qquad \frac{9}{4} = \frac{8}{4} + \frac{1}{4}$$
$$= \frac{8}{4} + \frac{1}{4} \qquad\qquad = 2 + \frac{1}{4}$$
$$= \frac{9}{4} \qquad\qquad\qquad = 2\frac{1}{4}$$

or

or

First, multiply the whole number by the denominator.

$2 \times 4 = 8$

Next, add the result to the numerator 1.

$8 + 1 = 9$

There are 9 quarters in $2\frac{1}{4}$.

$2\frac{1}{4} = \frac{9}{4}$

$\frac{9}{4} = 9 \div 4 = 2\,R\,1$

number of wholes

denominator → $4\overline{)9}$ ← numerator

$\frac{9}{4} = 2\frac{1}{4}$

Renaming Whole Numbers When Adding and Subtracting Fractions

Add fractions to get a sum greater than 1.	Subtract fractions from a whole number.
$\frac{3}{4} + \frac{1}{8} + \frac{3}{8}$	$2 - \frac{1}{6} - \frac{5}{12}$
$= \frac{6}{8} + \frac{1}{8} + \frac{3}{8}$	$= 1\frac{12}{12} - \frac{2}{12} - \frac{5}{12}$
$= \frac{10}{8}$	$= 1\frac{5}{12}$
$= 1\frac{2}{8}$	or
$= 1\frac{1}{4}$	$2 - \frac{1}{6} - \frac{5}{12}$
	$= \frac{24}{12} - \frac{2}{12} - \frac{5}{12}$
	$= \frac{17}{12}$
	$= 1\frac{5}{12}$

Solve Real-World Problems

A baker had 5 pounds of flour. He used $\frac{3}{4}$ pound to make muffins and $\frac{1}{8}$ pound to make bread. How much flour is left?

$$5 - \frac{3}{4} - \frac{1}{8} = 4\frac{8}{8} - \frac{6}{8} - \frac{1}{8}$$
$$= 4\frac{1}{8}$$

$4\frac{1}{8}$ pounds of flour are left.

Fraction of a Set

In a group of 12 flowers, 8 are pink. So, $\frac{2}{3}$ of the flowers are pink.

Solve Real-World Problems

Eliza had $36 and spent $\frac{7}{9}$ of it. How much did she have left?

$$\frac{7}{9} \times 36 = \frac{7}{9} \times 36$$
$$= 28$$
$$36 - 28 = 8$$

She had $8 left.

Overview:
- Bar models are applied to adding and subtracting fractions and finding a fraction of a set.
- Students use a fraction-of-a-whole model to multiply a fraction by a whole number.
- The fraction-of-a-set model and the unitary method are extended to modeling situations such as finding $\frac{2}{3}$ of 10 in Grade 5.

Problem Solving and Bar Models

Students have learned...

BIG IDEA
► Decimals can be added and subtracted in the same ways as whole numbers.

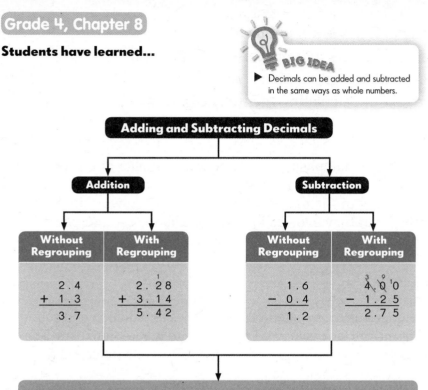

Adding and Subtracting Decimals

Addition

Without Regrouping	With Regrouping
2.4 + 1.3 3.7	2.²28 + 3.14 5.42

Subtraction

Without Regrouping	With Regrouping
1.6 − 0.4 1.2	³4.⁹0̸¹0 − 1.25 2.75

Real-World Problems

A pair of pants costs $36.49. A shirt costs $24.95. Victor has $55.00.
How much more money does he need to buy the pair of pants and the shirt?
Cost of pants + cost of shirt = total cost

$36.49 + $24.95 = $61.44

The total cost of the pair of pants and the shirt is $61.44.

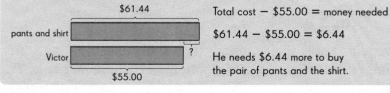

Total cost − $55.00 = money needed

$61.44 − $55.00 = $6.44

He needs $6.44 more to buy the pair of pants and the shirt.

Overview:

- Students in Grades 2 and 3 have used dollars and cents to model decimals.
- In Grade 4, decimal notation through hundredths is presented as an extension of the base-ten system.
- Addition and subtraction of decimals are developed using place-value chips.
- Emphasis is on two-step problems.
- Easy steps are done without bar models.
- Students experience solving problems involving addition and subtraction of decimals, with and without regrouping.

Mental Math and Estimation Strategies

The flexibility needed to calculate mentally is developed throughout the *Math in Focus*®: Singapore Math program. Beginning in Grade 1, children apply place-value concepts and properties of addition and subtraction to develop decomposition strategies for adding single-digit numbers. As new numbers and operations are introduced, flexible strategies that aid in calculating mentally continue to be introduced.

Grade 1

Students learn that place value and properties of addition and subtraction help them decompose numbers into tens and ones using number bonds. With this visual way of decomposing numbers, students learn to add and subtract numbers to 10, then to 20 and to 40, and finally to 100. Initially this strategy is used to help children to memorize basic facts, but later the decomposition strategies are applied to calculations with greater numbers.

Grade 2

Students also use number bonds based on place value and properties of addition and subtraction. Here, they decompose three-digit numbers to add multiples of hundreds, tens, and ones. By adding or subtracting a nearby ten and then adjusting the sum or difference, children can handle paper-and-pencil regrouping problems without needing to regroup in their heads.

Children are introduced to strategies for multiplying, such as skip-counting and using the Commutative Property of Multiplication to develop the multiplication facts. The most powerful of these strategies is to break a difficult product into two known products that can be added or subtracted. For example,

$$3 \times 8 \text{ can become } (3 \times 10) - (3 \times 2).$$

Because multiplying by 10 and 2 are familiar at this point, the expanded product becomes a mental math exercise. As the difficulty of the multiplication problems grows, this mental math strategy evolves into the familiar paper-and-pencil algorithm for multi-digit multiplication.

Grade 3

Students learn to extend the strategies for addition and subtraction based on place value and properties to greater numbers. They apply these strategies to estimating sums and differences.

The main focus in Grade 3 is on learning basic strategies for multiplying and dividing by single-digit whole numbers. Because students are encouraged to break products and quotients into two easier problems, computing mentally is a natural outgrowth. These strategies are applied to learning the basic facts for 6, 7, 8, and 9 and for multiplying multiples of 10 or 100, such as 8×90.

Grade 4

Students apply their mental-math skills to estimating sums, differences, products, and quotients of whole numbers. Each estimation strategy, such as rounding and front-end, relies on mental-math skills to arrive at a quick and easy solution.

Instructional Pathway for Transition

Grade 2: Chapter 10

Chapter 10: Mental Math and Estimation

Transition Topic: Mental Math

Grade 2 Chapter 10 Pre-Test Items	Grade 2 Chapter 10 Pre-Test Item Objective	Additional Support for the Objective: Grade 1 Reteach	Additional Support for the Objective: Grade 1 Extra Practice	Grade 1 Teacher Edition Support	Going Back Further (Grade K)
Items 4–5	Mentally add a one-digit number to a two-digit number.	1B pp. 95–96, 99	Lesson 14.1	1B Chapter 14 Lesson 1	
	Mentally add a two-digit number to tens.	1B pp. 97–98, 100	Lesson 14.1	1B Chapter 14 Lesson 1	
Items 6–7	Mentally subtract a one-digit number from a two-digit number.	1B pp. 101–102, 104	Lesson 14.2	1B Chapter 14 Lesson 2	
Item 8	Find the missing numbers in a pattern.	1B pp. 41, 43, 50	Lesson 12.3	1B Chapter 12 Lesson 3	
Item 11	Solve real-world (subtraction) problems.	1A pp. 143–146	Lesson 8.3	1B Chapter 19 Lesson 4	KB Chapter 20 Lesson 2 (coins and change)
Item 12	Solve real-world (addition) problems.	1B pp. 87–89	Lesson 13.6	1B Chapter 19 Lesson 4	KB Chapter 20 Lesson 2 (coins)
	Mentally subtract tens from a two-digit number.	1B pp. 103–104	Lesson 14.2	1B Chapter 14 Lesson 2	

For Additional Support: See the Grade 2 Chapter 10 Math in Focus Background Videos on Think Central <www-k6.thinkcentral.com>.

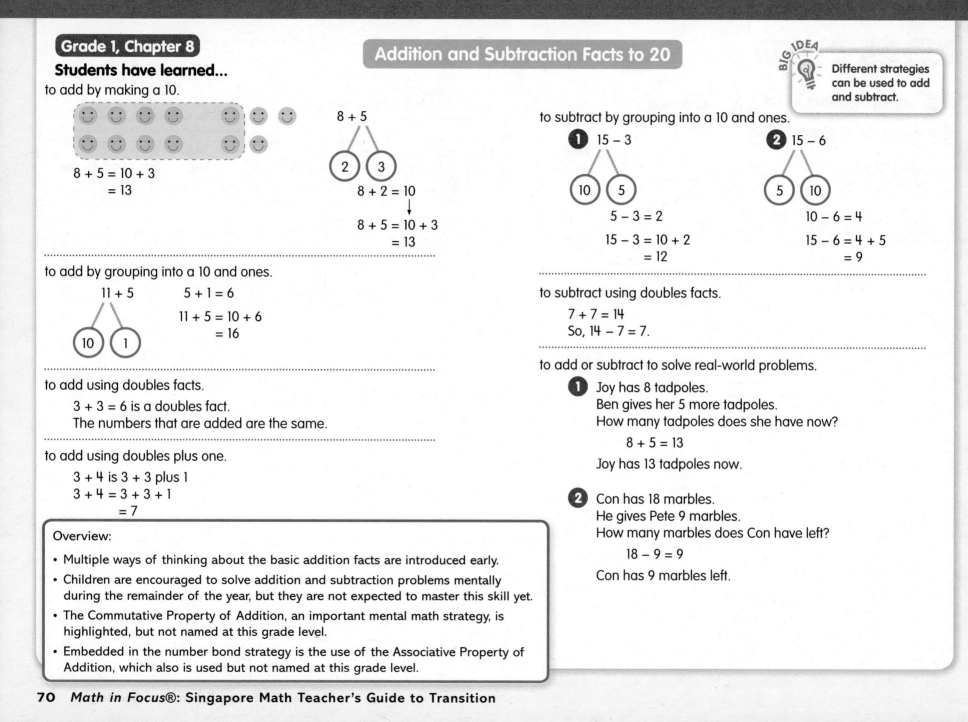

Students have learned...

to add by making a 10.

$8 + 5 = 10 + 3$
    $= 13$

$8 + 5$

2   3

$8 + 2 = 10$

$8 + 5 = 10 + 3$
    $= 13$

Addition and Subtraction Facts to 20

BIG IDEA
Different strategies can be used to add and subtract.

to add by grouping into a 10 and ones.

$11 + 5$

10   1

$5 + 1 = 6$

$11 + 5 = 10 + 6$
    $= 16$

to add using doubles facts.

$3 + 3 = 6$ is a doubles fact.
The numbers that are added are the same.

to add using doubles plus one.

$3 + 4$ is $3 + 3$ plus 1
$3 + 4 = 3 + 3 + 1$
    $= 7$

to subtract by grouping into a 10 and ones.

1 $15 - 3$

10   5

$5 - 3 = 2$

$15 - 3 = 10 + 2$
    $= 12$

2 $15 - 6$

5   10

$10 - 6 = 4$

$15 - 6 = 4 + 5$
    $= 9$

to subtract using doubles facts.

$7 + 7 = 14$
So, $14 - 7 = 7$.

to add or subtract to solve real-world problems.

1 Joy has 8 tadpoles.
Ben gives her 5 more tadpoles.
How many tadpoles does she have now?

$8 + 5 = 13$

Joy has 13 tadpoles now.

2 Con has 18 marbles.
He gives Pete 9 marbles.
How many marbles does Con have left?

$18 - 9 = 9$

Con has 9 marbles left.

Overview:

- Multiple ways of thinking about the basic addition facts are introduced early.
- Children are encouraged to solve addition and subtraction problems mentally during the remainder of the year, but they are not expected to master this skill yet.
- The Commutative Property of Addition, an important mental math strategy, is highlighted, but not named at this grade level.
- Embedded in the number bond strategy is the use of the Associative Property of Addition, which also is used but not named at this grade level.

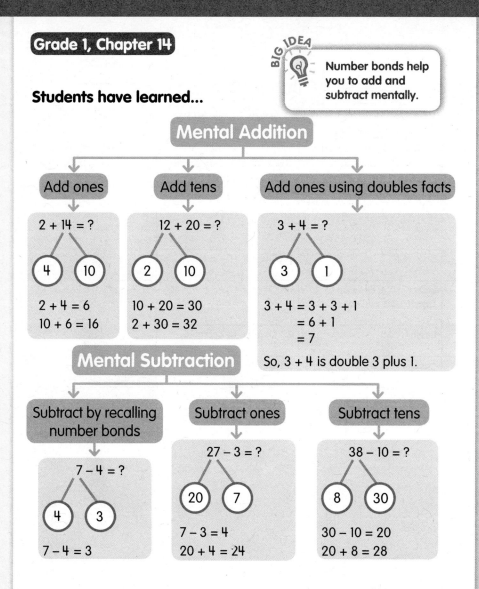

Grade 1, Chapter 14

BIG IDEA
Number bonds help you to add and subtract mentally.

Students have learned...

Mental Addition

Add ones

2 + 14 = ?

4   10

2 + 4 = 6
10 + 6 = 16

Add tens

12 + 20 = ?

2   10

10 + 20 = 30
2 + 30 = 32

Add ones using doubles facts

3 + 4 = ?

3   1

3 + 4 = 3 + 3 + 1
= 6 + 1
= 7

So, 3 + 4 is double 3 plus 1.

Mental Subtraction

Subtract by recalling number bonds

7 − 4 = ?

4   3

7 − 4 = 3

Subtract ones

27 − 3 = ?

20   7

7 − 3 = 4
20 + 4 = 24

Subtract tens

38 − 10 = ?

8   30

30 − 10 = 20
20 + 8 = 28

Overview:

- Composing and decomposing small numbers is a skill that children have practiced in previous chapters.

- They are now encouraged to use these strategies for mental calculations in order to eliminate the need to count on or use counters to derive answers.

- Drills of basic facts are not emphasized, but, because of the emphasis on calculating mentally, most children know their addition and subtraction facts by the end of Grade 1.

- Mental math strategies are then used to develop alternate algorithms to solve more complex computational and real-world problems.

Grade 3: Chapter 2

Chapter 2: Mental Math and Estimation

Transition Topic: Mental Math

Grade 3 Chapter 2 Pre-Test Items	Grade 3 Chapter 2 Pre-Test Item Objective	Additional Support for the Objective: Grade 2 Reteach	Additional Support for the Objective: Grade 2 Extra Practice	Grade 2 Teacher Edition Support	Going Back Further (Grade 1)
Item 2	Relate 'sum' to addition operation.	2B pp. 1–2	Lesson 10.1	2B Chapter 10 Lesson 1	
Items 5; 9; 11	Add up to three-digit numbers mentally with and without regrouping.	2B pp. 3–10; See also 1A pp. 21–28; 33–35	Lesson 10.2; See also Gr 1 Lessons 2.1 and 3.1	2B Chapter 10 Lesson 2	1B Chapter 14 Lesson 2 covers one-digit mental addition
Item 3	Relate 'difference' to subtraction operation.	2B pp. 11–12	Lesson 10.3	2B Chapter 10 Lesson 3	
Items 6; 10; 12	Subtract up to three-digit numbers mentally with and without regrouping.	2B pp. 13–20; See also 1A pp. 21–28; 51–54	Lesson 10.4; See also Gr 1 Lessons 2.1 and 4.1	2B Chapter 10 Lesson 4	1B Chapter 14 Lesson 2 covers one-digit mental addition
Items 1; 7–8	Use rounding to estimate sums and differences.	2B pp. 26–28	Lesson 10.5	2B Chapter 10 Lesson 5	
Item 4	Estimate to check reasonableness of answers.	2B pp. 26–28	Lesson 10.5	2B Chapter 10 Lesson 5	1B Chapter 16 Lesson 1 introduces estimating

For Additional Support: See the Grade 3 Chapter 2 Math in Focus Background Videos on Think Central <www-k6.thinkcentral.com>.

Mental Math and Estimation Strategies

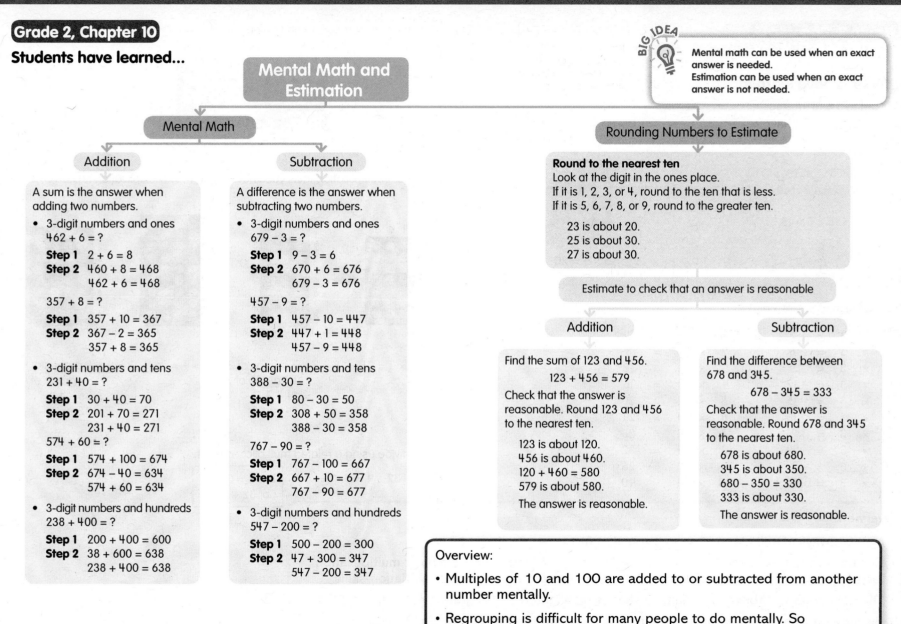

Grade 2, Chapter 10

Students have learned...

Mental Math and Estimation

BIG IDEA
Mental math can be used when an exact answer is needed.
Estimation can be used when an exact answer is not needed.

Mental Math

Addition

A sum is the answer when adding two numbers.

- 3-digit numbers and ones
462 + 6 = ?
Step 1 2 + 6 = 8
Step 2 460 + 8 = 468
462 + 6 = 468

357 + 8 = ?
Step 1 357 + 10 = 367
Step 2 367 − 2 = 365
357 + 8 = 365

- 3-digit numbers and tens
231 + 40 = ?
Step 1 30 + 40 = 70
Step 2 201 + 70 = 271
231 + 40 = 271
574 + 60 = ?
Step 1 574 + 100 = 674
Step 2 674 − 40 = 634
574 + 60 = 634

- 3-digit numbers and hundreds
238 + 400 = ?
Step 1 200 + 400 = 600
Step 2 38 + 600 = 638
238 + 400 = 638

Subtraction

A difference is the answer when subtracting two numbers.

- 3-digit numbers and ones
679 − 3 = ?
Step 1 9 − 3 = 6
Step 2 670 + 6 = 676
679 − 3 = 676

457 − 9 = ?
Step 1 457 − 10 = 447
Step 2 447 + 1 = 448
457 − 9 = 448

- 3-digit numbers and tens
388 − 30 = ?
Step 1 80 − 30 = 50
Step 2 308 + 50 = 358
388 − 30 = 358

767 − 90 = ?
Step 1 767 − 100 = 667
Step 2 667 + 10 = 677
767 − 90 = 677

- 3-digit numbers and hundreds
547 − 200 = ?
Step 1 500 − 200 = 300
Step 2 47 + 300 = 347
547 − 200 = 347

Rounding Numbers to Estimate

Round to the nearest ten
Look at the digit in the ones place.
If it is 1, 2, 3, or 4, round to the ten that is less.
If it is 5, 6, 7, 8, or 9, round to the greater ten.

23 is about 20.
25 is about 30.
27 is about 30.

Estimate to check that an answer is reasonable

Addition

Find the sum of 123 and 456.
123 + 456 = 579
Check that the answer is reasonable. Round 123 and 456 to the nearest ten.

123 is about 120.
456 is about 460.
120 + 460 = 580
579 is about 580.
The answer is reasonable.

Subtraction

Find the difference between 678 and 345.
678 − 345 = 333
Check that the answer is reasonable. Round 678 and 345 to the nearest ten.

678 is about 680.
345 is about 350.
680 − 350 = 330
333 is about 330.
The answer is reasonable.

Overview:

- Multiples of 10 and 100 are added to or subtracted from another number mentally.

- Regrouping is difficult for many people to do mentally. So students are taught a "work around" method that does not involve regrouping for mental calculations.

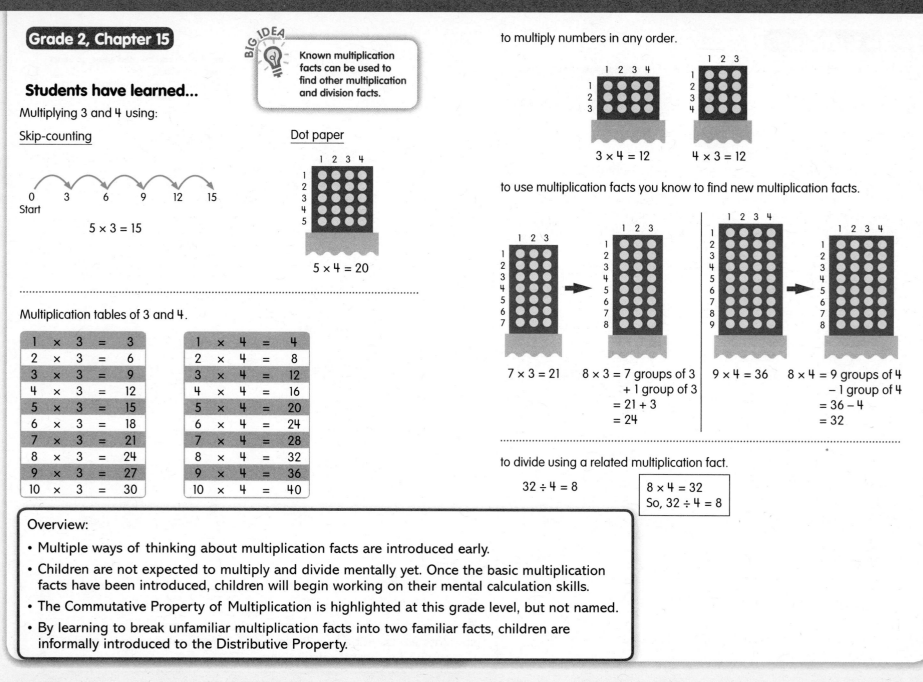

Grade 2, Chapter 15

BIG IDEA — Known multiplication facts can be used to find other multiplication and division facts.

Students have learned...

Multiplying 3 and 4 using:

Skip-counting

$5 \times 3 = 15$

Dot paper

$5 \times 4 = 20$

Multiplication tables of 3 and 4.

1	×	3	=	3		1	×	4	=	4
2	×	3	=	6		2	×	4	=	8
3	×	3	=	9		3	×	4	=	12
4	×	3	=	12		4	×	4	=	16
5	×	3	=	15		5	×	4	=	20
6	×	3	=	18		6	×	4	=	24
7	×	3	=	21		7	×	4	=	28
8	×	3	=	24		8	×	4	=	32
9	×	3	=	27		9	×	4	=	36
10	×	3	=	30		10	×	4	=	40

to multiply numbers in any order.

$3 \times 4 = 12$ $4 \times 3 = 12$

to use multiplication facts you know to find new multiplication facts.

$7 \times 3 = 21$

$8 \times 3 = 7$ groups of 3
+ 1 group of 3
= 21 + 3
= 24

$9 \times 4 = 36$

$8 \times 4 = 9$ groups of 4
− 1 group of 4
= 36 − 4
= 32

to divide using a related multiplication fact.

$32 \div 4 = 8$

$8 \times 4 = 32$
So, $32 \div 4 = 8$

Overview:

- Multiple ways of thinking about multiplication facts are introduced early.
- Children are not expected to multiply and divide mentally yet. Once the basic multiplication facts have been introduced, children will begin working on their mental calculation skills.
- The Commutative Property of Multiplication is highlighted at this grade level, but not named.
- By learning to break unfamiliar multiplication facts into two familiar facts, children are informally introduced to the Distributive Property.

Instructional Pathway for Transition

Grade 4: Chapter 2

Chapter 2: Estimation and Number Theory

Transition Topic: Mental Math

Grade 4 Chapter 2 Pre-Test Items	Grade 4 Chapter 2 Pre-Test Item Objective	Additional Support for the Objective: Grade 3 Reteach	Additional Support for the Objective: Grade 3 Extra Practice	Grade 3 Teacher Edition Support	Going Back Further (Grade 2)
	Add and subtract two-digit numbers mentally with or without regrouping.	3A pp. 17–30; See also 1A pp. 21–30; 33–35	Lessons 2.1–2.3; See also Gr 1 Lesson 2.1	3A Chapter 2 Lesson 3	2B Chapter 10 Lessons 2 and 4
Items 1; 3; 6–9; 16–17	Round numbers to estimate sums and differences.	3A pp. 31–38	Lesson 2.4	3A Chapter 2 Lesson 4	2B Chapter 10 Lesson 5
Items 2; 4; 10–11	Use front-end estimation to estimate sums and differences.	3A pp. 39–40	Lesson 2.5	3A Chapter 2 Lesson 5	2B Chapter 10 Lessons 2 and 4 (informal)

For Additional Support: See the Grade 4 Chapter 2 Math in Focus Background Videos on Think Central <www-k6.thinkcentral.com>.

Mental Math and Estimation Strategies

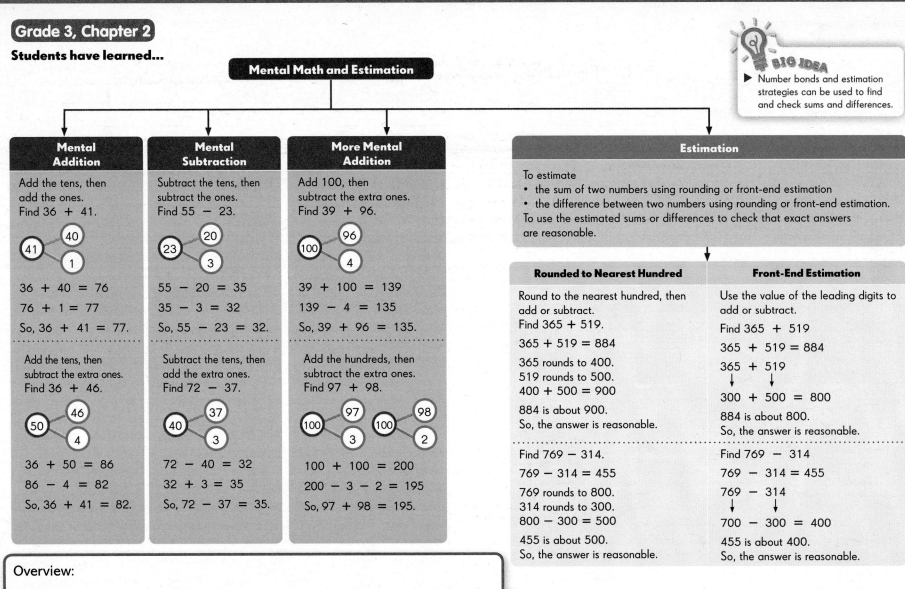

Grade 3, Chapter 2

Students have learned...

Mental Math and Estimation

BIG IDEA
► Number bonds and estimation strategies can be used to find and check sums and differences.

Mental Addition

Add the tens, then add the ones.
Find 36 + 41.

41 — 40 / 1

36 + 40 = 76
76 + 1 = 77
So, 36 + 41 = 77.

Add the tens, then subtract the extra ones.
Find 36 + 46.

50 — 46 / 4

36 + 50 = 86
86 − 4 = 82
So, 36 + 41 = 82.

Mental Subtraction

Subtract the tens, then subtract the ones.
Find 55 − 23.

23 — 20 / 3

55 − 20 = 35
35 − 3 = 32
So, 55 − 23 = 32.

Subtract the tens, then add the extra ones.
Find 72 − 37.

40 — 37 / 3

72 − 40 = 32
32 + 3 = 35
So, 72 − 37 = 35.

More Mental Addition

Add 100, then subtract the extra ones.
Find 39 + 96.

100 — 96 / 4

39 + 100 = 139
139 − 4 = 135
So, 39 + 96 = 135.

Add the hundreds, then subtract the extra ones.
Find 97 + 98.

100 — 97 / 3   100 — 98 / 2

100 + 100 = 200
200 − 3 − 2 = 195
So, 97 + 98 = 195.

Estimation

To estimate
• the sum of two numbers using rounding or front-end estimation
• the difference between two numbers using rounding or front-end estimation.
To use the estimated sums or differences to check that exact answers are reasonable.

Rounded to Nearest Hundred	Front-End Estimation
Round to the nearest hundred, then add or subtract. Find 365 + 519. 365 + 519 = 884 365 rounds to 400. 519 rounds to 500. 400 + 500 = 900 884 is about 900. So, the answer is reasonable.	Use the value of the leading digits to add or subtract. Find 365 + 519 365 + 519 = 884 365 + 519 ↓ ↓ 300 + 500 = 800 884 is about 800. So, the answer is reasonable.
Find 769 − 314. 769 − 314 = 455 769 rounds to 800. 314 rounds to 300. 800 − 300 = 500 455 is about 500. So, the answer is reasonable.	Find 769 − 314 769 − 314 = 455 769 − 314 ↓ ↓ 700 − 300 = 400 455 is about 400. So, the answer is reasonable.

Overview:

• Mental math strategies for addition and subtraction that were introduced in Grade 2 are extended to numbers greater than 100.

• The mental math strategies are applied to estimating sums and differences.

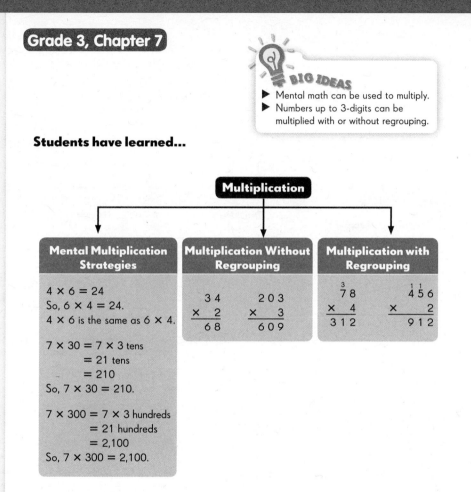

Grade 3, Chapter 7

BIG IDEAS
▶ Mental math can be used to multiply.
▶ Numbers up to 3-digits can be multiplied with or without regrouping.

Students have learned...

Multiplication

Mental Multiplication Strategies	Multiplication Without Regrouping	Multiplication with Regrouping

Mental Multiplication Strategies:

4 × 6 = 24
So, 6 × 4 = 24.
4 × 6 is the same as 6 × 4.

7 × 30 = 7 × 3 tens
　　　 = 21 tens
　　　 = 210
So, 7 × 30 = 210.

7 × 300 = 7 × 3 hundreds
　　　 = 21 hundreds
　　　 = 2,100
So, 7 × 300 = 2,100.

Multiplication Without Regrouping:

```
  34          203
×  2        ×   3
----        -----
  68          609
```

Multiplication with Regrouping:

```
  3            1 1
  78          456
×  4        ×   2
----        -----
 312          912
```

Overview:

• In Grades 1 and 2, students have been taught multiplication as repeated addition and division as sharing equally.

• Students learn to mentally multiply any multiple of 10 or 100 by a one-digit number using basic facts.

• This informal use of the Associative Property of Multiplication justifies this strategy. For example, writing 7 × 30 as 7 × 3 tens and then multiplying can be written as:

$$7 \times (3 \times 10) = (7 \times 3) \times 10.$$

• The concept of place value is used to help students multiply using vertical form.

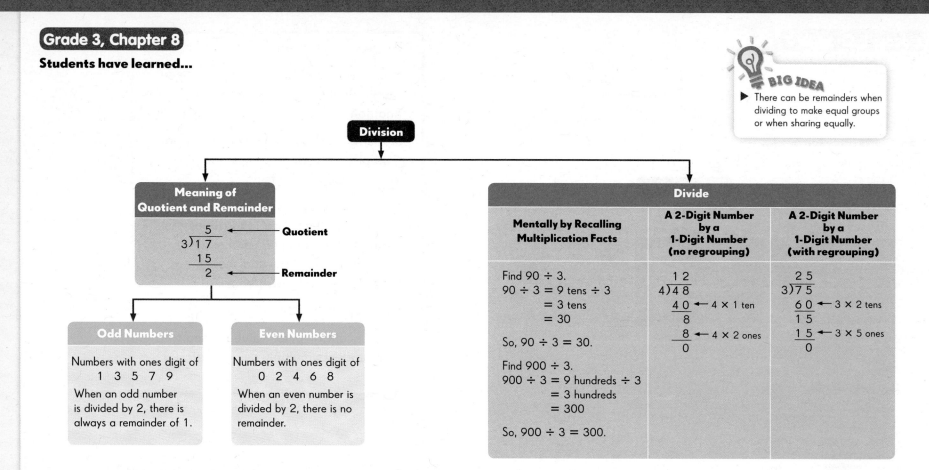

Grade 3, Chapter 8

Students have learned...

BIG IDEA

▶ There can be remainders when dividing to make equal groups or when sharing equally.

Division

Meaning of Quotient and Remainder

$$\begin{array}{r} 5 \\ 3\overline{)17} \\ \underline{15} \\ 2 \end{array}$$ ← Quotient

← Remainder

Odd Numbers

Numbers with ones digit of
1 3 5 7 9

When an odd number is divided by 2, there is always a remainder of 1.

Even Numbers

Numbers with ones digit of
0 2 4 6 8

When an even number is divided by 2, there is no remainder.

Divide

Mentally by Recalling Multiplication Facts	A 2-Digit Number by a 1-Digit Number (no regrouping)	A 2-Digit Number by a 1-Digit Number (with regrouping)
Find 90 ÷ 3. 90 ÷ 3 = 9 tens ÷ 3 = 3 tens = 30 So, 90 ÷ 3 = 30. Find 900 ÷ 3. 900 ÷ 3 = 9 hundreds ÷ 3 = 3 hundreds = 300 So, 900 ÷ 3 = 300.	$$\begin{array}{r} 1\,2 \\ 4\overline{)4\,8} \\ \underline{4\,0} \\ 8 \\ \underline{8} \\ 0 \end{array}$$ ← 4 × 1 ten ← 4 × 2 ones	$$\begin{array}{r} 2\,5 \\ 3\overline{)7\,5} \\ \underline{6\,0} \\ 1\,5 \\ \underline{1\,5} \\ 0 \end{array}$$ ← 3 × 2 tens ← 3 × 5 ones

Overview:

• Strategies for dividing mentally are related to strategies for multiplying mentally.

• By thinking of 90 as 9 tens and 900 as 9 hundreds, these numbers can be divided by one-digit numbers using basic facts.

• This strategy is continued throughout the program and is used effectively to divide numbers such as 9 tenths (0.9) or 9 twentieths $\left(\frac{9}{20}\right)$ by a one-digit number.

• Division concepts are extended to division situations where there may be remainders.

Grade 5: Chapter 1

Chapter 1: Whole Numbers

Transition Topic: Mental Math					
Grade 5 Chapter 1 Pre-Test Items	Grade 5 Chapter 1 Pre-Test Item Objective	Additional Support for the Objective: Grade 4 Reteach	Additional Support for the Objective: Grade 4 Extra Practice	Grade 4 Teacher Edition Support	Going Back Further (Grade 3)
Items 3–4, 11–15; 16–18	Round numbers to estimate sums, differences, products, and quotients. Estimate to check that an answer is reasonable.	4A pp. 19–28	Lesson 2.1	4A Chapter 2 Lesson 1	Grade 3 students divide numbers by a one-digit number without regrouping or remainders in 3A Chapter 8 Lesson 4
Items 16–17, 19	Estimate products and quotients.	4A pp. 64–68; 78–80	Lessons 3.2 and 3.4	4A Chapter 2 Lesson 1	

For Additional Support: See the Grade 5 Chapter 1 Math in Focus Background Videos on Think Central <www-k6.thinkcentral.com>.

Grade 4, Chapter 2

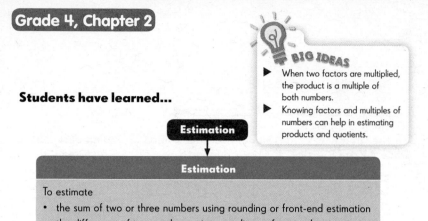

💡 **BIG IDEAS**

▶ When two factors are multiplied, the product is a multiple of both numbers.

▶ Knowing factors and multiples of numbers can help in estimating products and quotients.

Students have learned...

Estimation

Estimation

To estimate
- the sum of two or three numbers using rounding or front-end estimation
- the difference of two numbers using rounding or front-end estimation
- the product of a 3-digit number and a 1-digit number using rounding or front-end estimation of the 3-digit number
- the quotient when a 3-digit number is divided by a 1-digit number using related multiplication facts.

To decide whether to estimate or find an exact answer.

Round to the Nearest Hundred	Front-End Estimation
$147 + 781 = 928 \rightarrow 100 + 800 = 900$	$147 + 781$ $100 + 700 = 800$
$8,412 - 1,951 \rightarrow 8,400 - 2,000$ $= 6,461 \qquad\quad = 6,400$	$8,412 - 1,951$ $8,000 - 1,000 = 7,000$
$267 \times 7 = 1,869 \rightarrow 300 \times 7 = 2,100$	$267 \times 7 = 1,869$ $200 \times 7 = 1,400$

Estimate Quotients Using Related Multiplication Facts

- To estimate $546 \div 6$,
  $6 \times 90 = 540 \qquad 6 \times 100 = 600$
  546 is closer to 540 than to 600. $540 \div 6 = 90$
  The estimated quotient is 90.

Overview:

- The ability to do mental math is crucial for assessing the reasonableness of results.

- Mental math strategies are applied to estimating sums, differences, products, and quotients.

- The division strategy "Using Related Multiplication Facts" is often called "Using Compatible Numbers" in other programs.

- Students are introduced to factors, multiples, least common multiples, and greatest common factors.